Holt
Mathematics

Course 1

Alternate Openers:

Explorations Transparencies

D1158826

HOLT, RINEHART AND WINSTON

A Harcourt Education Company

Orlando • **Austin** • New York • San Diego • London

ISBN 0-03-078149-3

1 2 3 4 5   141   09 08 07 06

CONTENTS

1-1 Comparing and Ordering Whole Numbers

Values **increase** as you move **right** on a number line.

Values **decrease** as you move **left** on a number line.

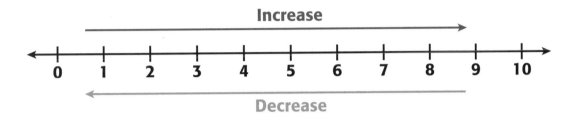

The number line below shows some large whole numbers between 1,000 and 1,100.

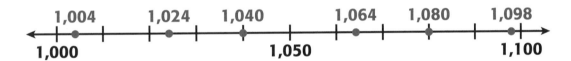

Compare the numbers from the number line above. Write < or >.

1. 1,024 $\boxed{<}$ 1,080

2. 1,024 $\boxed{>}$ 1,004

3. 1,064 $\boxed{>}$ 1,040

4. 1,004 $\boxed{<}$ 1,040

5. 1,040 $\boxed{>}$ 1,024

6. 1,064 $\boxed{<}$ 1,098

Think and Discuss

7. Explain how to use a number line to compare whole numbers. Possible answer: Numbers to the right are greater than numbers to the left.

8. Describe how to use place value to compare the numbers 1,004 and 1,040. Possible answer: Compare digits in corresponding place values from left to right until the digits differ. The number whose digit is greater is the greater number.

Holt Mathematics

1-2 Estimating with Whole Numbers

Harvard Middle School is collecting aluminum cans to recycle for a fund-raiser. The number of cans that each grade collected is shown in the bar graph.

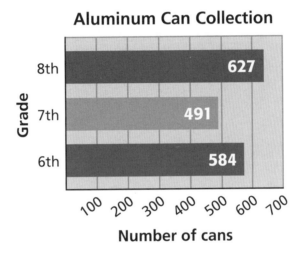

Aluminum Can Collection

1. Estimate the total number of cans that Harvard Middle School collected. Possible answer: 1,700

The principal announced that nearly 2,000 cans were collected. The newspaper reported that over 1,700 cans were collected.

2. Is either of these reports correct? Yes; both are correct.

3. Why are the reports different? Possible answer: Different rounding methods were used.

Think and Discuss

4. **Describe** how you reached your estimate. Possible answer: Round to the nearest hundred and add.

5. **Identify** some words that indicate whether an amount is an estimate or approximation. Possible answer: nearly, almost, about, approximately

Holt Mathematics

1-3 Exponents

1. Maria won the grand prize on a game show. She will be given $2 the first month, $4 the second month, $8 the third month, and so on as her payment is doubled each month for one year.

   a. Complete the table.

   b. How much will Maria receive in the fifth month? $32

   c. How much will Maria receive in the eighth month? $256

   d. Use a calculator to determine how much Maria will receive in the last month of the year. $4,096

Month	Amount ($)
1	2
2	4
3	8
4	16
5	32
6	64
7	128
8	256

Think and Discuss

2. **Describe** the pattern in the table. Possible answer: The dollar amount doubles each month.

3. **Explain** how the values in the table compare with the values 2, 2^2, 2^3, 2^4, and so on. Possible answer: The values in the Amount column are equal to 2, 2^2, 2^3, 2^4, and so on.

Holt Mathematics

1-4 Order of Operations

Calculators are programmed to perform operations in a certain order. Each keystroke sequence below results in 17.

For each keystroke sequence, determine the order of operations the calculator follows.

1. (2 + 3) × 5 ENTER $2 + 3 = 5, 5 \cdot 5 = 25$

2. 2 ∧ 3 – 1 × 4 ENTER $2^3 = 8, 1 \cdot 4 = 4, 8 - 4 = 4$

3. 2 ∧ (3 – 1) × 4 ENTER $3 - 1 = 2, 2^2 = 4, 4 \cdot 4 = 16$

Write the keystroke sequence for each expression.

4. $5 - 2^2$ 5 ⊟ 2 ⋀ 2

5. $(2 - 3)^3 + 2$ ⟮ 2 ⊟ 3 ⟯ ⋀ 3 ⊞ 2

Think and Discuss

6. Explain why there needs to be a rule for the order of operations. Possible answer: to ensure that everyone can agree on one correct answer

Holt Mathematics

EXPLORATION

1-5 Mental Math

1. Choose one expression from each pair to evaluate using mental math.

   a. $25 \cdot 24$ $(25 \cdot 4) \cdot 6$ 600

   b. $5 \cdot 22$ $(5 \cdot 20) + (5 \cdot 2)$ 110

   c. $13 + 44 + 27$ $44 + (13 + 27)$ 84

   d. $41 + 32 + 9 + 18$ $(41 + 9) + (32 + 18)$ 100

2. What makes the expressions you chose easier to evaluate?
Possible answer: Numbers are grouped in a way that makes calculations easier.

3. What makes the expressions you did not choose more difficult to evaluate? Possible answer: Numbers are not grouped in ways that simplify calculations.

Think and Discuss

4. **Discuss** the mental math strategies you used.

5. **Compare** the first expression with the second expression in each pair. How are they alike? How are they different?

   4. Possible answer: Group numbers that add or multiply to a multiple of 10 or 100.

   5. Possible answer: The expressions in each pair are equivalent. The numbers in the right column have been grouped to make calculations easier.

Holt Mathematics

1-6 Choose the Method of Computation

Decide whether you would use mental math, pencil and paper, or a calculator to solve each problem. Then solve.

1. Susan makes $9.50 per hour. She worked 7 hours on Monday, 8 hours on Tuesday, 5 hours on Wednesday, and 10 hours on Friday. What is the total amount that Susan earned for the week? $285

2. Carlos is saving his money to buy a new bike. He earns $45 each week doing yard work, and the bike costs $189. How many weeks will he have to work to have enough money to buy the bike? 5 weeks

3. At a basketball game, 9,980 tickets were sold at $22 each. Find the total amount of money from ticket sales. $219,560

4. Rina counted the following numbers of books on each shelf in the storeroom: 24, 47, 26, 53, and 39. Find the total number of books. 189

5. A group of 12 people wants to rent a room at a pizza restaurant for a party. The room costs $75 to rent. Will $6 from each person be enough to cover the rent?
12 · 6 = 72, so $6 per person will not be enough.

Think and Discuss

6. **Discuss** when you might choose to use mental math. Possible answer: Use mental math when the problem involves compatible numbers or if an estimate is needed.

7. **Explain** how you decide whether to use pencil and paper or a calculator when you choose not to use mental math.
Possible answer: Use paper and pencil if there are not many calculations and the numbers are reasonably easy to work with.

Holt Mathematics

EXPLORATION

1-7 Patterns and Sequences

1. Examine the sequence of figures below and look for a pattern.

   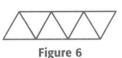

Figure 1   Figure 2   Figure 3   Figure 4   Figure 5   Figure 6

a. Sketch the next two figures in your pattern. Count the number of line segments it takes to draw each.

b. Copy and complete the table for your pattern.

Figure Number	1	2	3	4	5	6	7	8	9	10
Number of Line Segments	3	5	7	9	11	13	15	17	19	21

Find the next three numbers in each sequence.

2. 1, 3, 5, 7, __9__, __11__, __13__, …

3. 96, 84, 72, __60__, __48__, __36__, …

4. 1, 3, 6, 10, 15, __21__, __28__, __36__, …

Think and Discuss

5. **Describe** the pattern you noticed in the sequence of triangles. Possible answer: Each figure requires two more segments than the previous one.

6. **Explain** how you found the next three numbers in numbers 2–4. Possible answer: Look for an addition or subtraction pattern to go from one number to the next.

Holt Mathematics

2-1 Variables and Expressions

1. Look at the sequence of connected squares.

1 + 3   1 + 3 + 3   1 + 3 + 3 + 3

a. Sketch the next two squares. □□□□ □□□□□

b. To complete the table for the connected squares, count the number of segments it takes to draw each square.

Number of Connected Squares	1	2	3	4	5	10	20	100
Number of Segments	4	7	10	13	16	31	61	301

c. How can you find the number of segments if you know the number of squares? Multiply the number of squares by 3 and then add 1.

Think and Discuss

2. **Explain** the reasoning you used to find the number of segments in one hundred connected squares.

3. **Explain** the reasoning you could use to find the number of segments in one thousand connected squares.

2. Possible answer: Multiply 100 by 3 and then add 1.

3. Possible answer: Multiply 1,000 by 3 and then add 1.

Holt Mathematics

EXPLORATION

2-2 Translate Between Words and Math

Drawing pictures and using formulas can help you translate between words and math.

A basketball court is 50 ft wide by 94 ft long. What is its area?

Formula for area

$A =$ length $\times$ width

$A = 94 \times 50$

$A = 4{,}700$

The area is 4,700 ft^2.

Area = ?	50 ft

94 ft

In some word problems, word order may be confusing. For example, the following problems can be translated in at least two different ways.

Rewrite each problem to make it clearer.

	Word Problem	Possible Translations	Better Word Problem
1.	Write the expression "4 times x plus 6."	$4x + 6$ or $4(x + 6)$	The product of 4 and x increased by 6: $4x + 6$ 4 times the sum of x and 6: $4(x + 6)$
2.	Translate "the square root of n minus 3."	$\sqrt{n} - 3$ or $\sqrt{n - 3}$	3 less than the square root of n: $\sqrt{n} - 3$ The square root of the difference of n and 3: $\sqrt{n - 3}$

Think and Discuss

3. Explain what you did to rewrite numbers 1 and 2 to make them easier to translate into math. Possible answer: Identify the main operation rather than translating from left to right.

Holt Mathematics

2-3 Translating Between Tables and Expressions

You can explore geometric patterns to help you write algebraic expressions. Consider this sequence of figures.

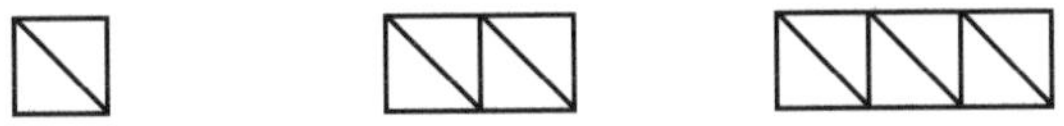

Figure 1   **Figure 2**   **Figure 3**

The first figure has 5 segments, the second figure has 9 segments, and the third figure has 13 segments.

Figure Number	1	2	3
Number of Segments	5	9	13

1. Draw the next two figures in the pattern.

    Figure 4   **Figure 5**

2. Complete the table.

Figure Number	1	2	3	4	5
Number of Segments	5	9	13	17	21

3. Describe any patterns you notice in the table. **Possible answer: The number of segments is 4 times the figure number plus 1.**

Think and Discuss

4. **Explain** how you can find the number of segments in the 6th figure without drawing it. **Possible answer: Multiply 6 by 4 and then add 1. There are 25 segments.**

5. **Explain** Explain how you can find the number of segments in any figure in the pattern if you know the number of the figure.

    Possible answer: Multiply the figure number by 4 and then add 1.

Holt Mathematics

EXPLORATION

2-4 Equations and Their Solutions

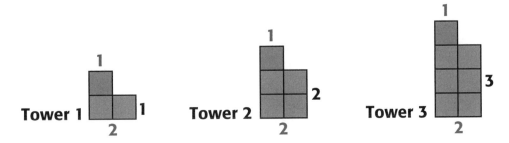

Tower 1   Tower 2   Tower 3

In the sequence of towers, the base of each tower is always 2 squares wide. The heights of the towers vary. If we call the height of each tower h, we can represent this pattern with the following expression:

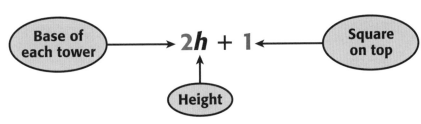

1. Use the pattern in the sequence of towers to draw a tower with 11 squares. Which tower number is it in the sequence? tower 5

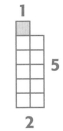

2. Use the pattern to solve the equation $2h + 1 = 21$. $h = 10$

3. Look at the sequence of grids and draw a picture of the grid that has 10 shaded squares.

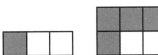

   a. Where in the sequence does this grid occur? grid 4

   b. Write an equation for the problem in **3a**. $3n - 2 = 10$

Think and Discuss

4. **Discuss** what is meant by "a solution of an equation." Possible answer: A solution of an equation is a value of the variable that makes the equation true.

Holt Mathematics

2-5 Addition Equations

How much change from a dollar do you get when you buy something that costs 51 cents?

This problem can also be expressed as **what number** plus **51** is **100**?

$$n + 51 = 100$$
$$\downarrow$$
$$49 + 51 = 100$$
$$\longrightarrow n = 49 \qquad \text{The change is 49¢.}$$

Find the value of n in each equation.

1. $4 + n = 100$ $n =$ _____96_____

2. $n + 45 = 100$ $n =$ _____55_____

3. $19 + n = 100$ $n =$ _____81_____

4. $n + 65 = 100$ $n =$ _____35_____

5. $100 = 41 + n$ $n =$ _____59_____

Think and Discuss

6. Discuss your strategies for solving the equations.

7. Explain how you can mentally find the solution to $n + 125 = 500$.

6. Possible answer: Subtract the number on the left side of the equation from 100.

7. Possible answer: Start with 125. Add 75 to get 200. Add 300 to get 500.

So $n = 75 + 300 = 375$.

Holt Mathematics

2-6 Subtraction Equations

After spending $11, Jane has $3 left in her purse. How much did she have to begin with?

Beginning amount $11 spent   Amount left

        3

$$n - 11 = 3$$
$$\downarrow$$
$$14 - 11 = 3$$

$n = 14$ She had $14 to begin with.

Find the value of *n* in each equation.

1. $n - 25 = 75$ $n = $ ___100___

2. $n - 4 = 19$ $n = $ ___23___

3. $n - 7 = 35$ $n = $ ___42___

4. $n - 14 = 21$ $n = $ ___35___

5. $n - 20 = 83$ $n = $ ___103___

Think and Discuss

6. Describe your strategies for solving the subtraction equations. **Possible answer: Add the number being subtracted to both sides of the equation.**

7. Explain how you can find the solution to $n - 125 = 375$.
Possible answer: Add 375 + 125 = 500.

Holt Mathematics

2-7 Multiplication Equations

Bill bought 7 tickets to a basketball game for $21. How much did each ticket cost?

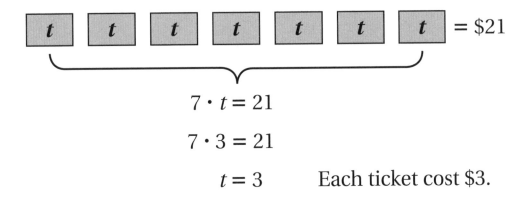

$$7 \cdot t = 21$$
$$7 \cdot 3 = 21$$
$$t = 3 \qquad \text{Each ticket cost \$3.}$$

Find the value of n in each equation.

1. $4 \cdot n = 36$ $n = \underline{\hspace{1cm} 9 \hspace{1cm}}$

2. $100 \cdot n = 500$ $n = \underline{\hspace{1cm} 5 \hspace{1cm}}$

3. $50 = 5 \cdot n$ $n = \underline{\hspace{1cm} 10 \hspace{1cm}}$

4. $24 \cdot n = 48$ $n = \underline{\hspace{1cm} 2 \hspace{1cm}}$

5. $10 \cdot n = 240$ $n = \underline{\hspace{1cm} 24 \hspace{1cm}}$

Think and Discuss

6. Discuss your strategies for solving the equations.

7. Explain how you can find the solution to $4 \cdot n = 200$.

6.   Possible answer: Divide both sides of the equation by the number by which the variable is multiplied.

7.   Possible answer: Divide $200 \div 4 = 50$.

Holt Mathematics

2-8 Division Equations

Four friends decided to share the cost of a gift for their dance teacher. After dividing the cost by 4, each friend's share is $25. What was the cost of the gift?

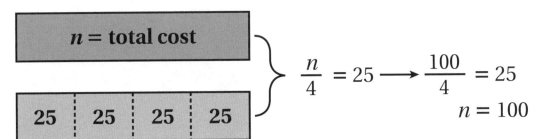

$$\frac{n}{4} = 25 \longrightarrow \frac{100}{4} = 25$$

$$n = 100$$

The gift cost $100.

Find the value of *n* in each equation.

1. $\frac{n}{2} = 50$

$n = $ ___100___

2. $\frac{n}{10} = 2$

$n = $ ___20___

3. $20 = \frac{n}{3}$

$n = $ ___60___

4. $\frac{n}{7} = 5$

$n = $ ___35___

Think and Discuss

5. Discuss your strategies for solving the equations.

6. Explain how you can find the solution to $\frac{n}{2} = 26$.

5. Possible answer: Multiply both sides of the equation by the number in the denominator of the fraction.

6. Possible answer: Multiply $2 \cdot 26 = 52$.

Holt Mathematics

3-1 Representing, Comparing, and Ordering Decimals

To model a decimal,

- color a 10-by-10-square grid for each whole in the decimal,

- color one 10-by-1-square strip for each tenth in the decimal, and color a small square for each hundredth in the decimal.

For example, the graph paper models the decimal 1.62.

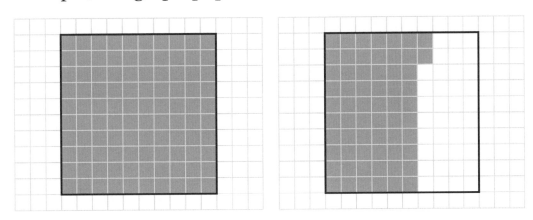

1. Draw a model for each decimal.

   a. 1.25   **b.** 2.13   **c.** 1.70   **d.** 1.7

2. Compare the models for **1c** and **1d.** What do you notice about these two decimals? They are the same.

3. Order the decimals in numbers **1a–1d** from least to greatest. Explain your reasoning. 1.25, 1.7, 2.13; the decimals are ordered from the least number of shaded squares to the greatest number of shaded squares.

Think and Discuss

4. **Explain** why 0.4 = 0.40. 4 tenths is the same as 40 hundredths.

5. **Explain** why 0.5 is greater than 0.10 even though 10 is greater than 5. Possible answer: 0.5 = 0.50 and 50 > 10.

1a.    b.   c. 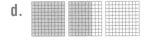   d.

Holt Mathematics

3-2 Estimating Decimals

For each problem, estimate a solution. Then compute with a calculator to see how close your estimated solutions are to the actual solutions. Estimates may vary.

		Estimate	Actual
1.	Seven people want to share the cost of a $33.75 boat rental. How much will each person pay?	$\frac{35}{7} = \$5$	$4.82
2.	You purchase items that cost the following amounts: $4.95, $1.29, $6.67, $4.19, and $10.39. What is the total cost?	$27	$27.49
3.	How much change is there from $200.00 for an item that costs $157.98?	$40	$42.02
4.	Ron's gas tank holds 21 gallons and is empty. If gas costs $2.499 per gallon, how much will it cost to fill Ron's tank?	20(2.5) = $50	$52.48

Think and Discuss

5. **Discuss** the estimation strategies you used.

6. **Describe** a situation in which all you need is an estimated solution and a situation in which you must calculate an exact solution. Possible answer: estimate: number of people at a parade; exact: batting average

5. Possible answer: For Exercises 1 and 4, use compatible numbers. For Exercises 2 and 3, round to the nearest dollar and nearest ten.

Holt Mathematics

EXPLORATION

3-3 Adding and Subtracting Decimals

You have 19¢. How much more do you need to have $1.00? From 19¢ to 20¢, add 1¢. From 20¢ to $1.00, add 80¢. The answer is 1¢ + 80¢, or 81¢.

1. Draw arrows to connect each pair of amounts that would give you a sum of $1.00.

Amount 1	Amount 2
$0.19	$0.63
$0.25	$0.55
$0.76	$0.93
$0.07	$0.75
$0.65	$0.24
$0.37	$0.35
$0.45	**$0.81**

2. Compute the change from $10.00 on a purchase of each amount. Example: From $1.25 to $2.00, add $0.75. From $2.00 to $10.00, add $8.00. So the change on a purchase of $1.25 is $0.75 + $8.00 = $8.75.

Amount	Change from $10.00
$1.25	**$8.75**
$2.76	$7.24
$3.07	$6.93
$4.65	$5.35
$5.37	$4.63
$6.45	$3.55
$7.59	$2.41

Think and Discuss

3. **Name** five different pairs of numbers that each have a sum of $1.00. Possible answer: $0.05 + $0.95; $0.10 + $0.90; $0.15 + $0.85; $0.20 + $0.80; $0.25 + $0.75

4. **Describe** how you can use the strategy of "adding up" to find 200 − 176.25. Possible answer: From 176.25 to 177, add 0.75. From 177 to 200, add 23. So 200 − 176.25 = 23.75.

18

Holt Mathematics

3-4 Scientific Notation

You can use exponents to represent powers of 10.

$10^1 = 10$

$10^2 = 10 \times 10 = 100$

$10^3 = 10 \times 10 \times 10 = 1,000$

$10^4 = 10 \times 10 \times 10 \times 10 = 10,000$

Find each product.

1. 6.25×10^1 **2.** 6.25×10^2 **3.** 6.25×10^3 **4.** 6.25×10^4
    62.5   625   6,250   62,500

In scientific notation, numbers are written as the product of a power of 10 and a number that is greater than 1 and less than 10.

Number	Scientific Notation
6,250	6.25×10^3
62.50	6.25×10^1
625	6.25×10^2

Write each number in scientific notation by filling in the exponent for the power of 10.

5. $42.5 = 4.25 \times 10^{\square}$ 1   **6.** $425 = 4.25 \times 10^{\square}$ 2

7. $4250 = 4.25 \times 10^{\square}$ 3   **8.** $42500 = 4.25 \times 10^{\square}$ 4

Think and Discuss

Possible answer: $10^3 = 1,000$, so 5.3×10^3 must be

9. Explain why 5.3×10^3 is greater than 1,000. greater than 1,000.

10. Explain how you know that $6.25 \times 10^6 = 6,250,000$.

Possible answer: $10^6 = 1,000,000$, so $6.25 \times 10^6 = 6,250,000$.

Holt Mathematics

3-5 Multiplying Decimals

When you multiply decimals, you can use estimation to help you determine the position of the decimal point in the product.

Estimate each product. Then use a calculator to see how reasonable your estimate is. Possible answers:

		Estimate	Actual
1.	4.235×16.9	$4(17) = 68$	71.5715
2.	0.78×568	$\frac{3}{4}(600) = 450$	443.04
3.	56.1×23	$60(20) = 1{,}200$	1,290.3
4.	15.6×2.15	$16(2) = 32$	33.54

Estimate each product. Use this estimate to decide where to place a decimal point in the answer. Check with your calculator.

5. $70.5 \times 4.4 = 3 \ 1 \ 0.2$

6. $0.75 \times 692 = 5 \ 1 \ 9.0$

7. $56 \times 3.125 = 1 \ 7 \ 5.0$

8. $45.6 \times 2.15 = 9 \ 8.0 \ 4$

9. $4.17 \times 1.2 = 5.0 \ 0 \ 4$

10. $125.2 \times 7.4 = 9 \ 2 \ 6.4 \ 8$

Think and Discuss

11. Discuss your strategies for estimating in numbers 1–4.
Possible answer: Round up or down to a compatible number, and then multiply.

12. Explain how you know where to place the decimal point in a product. Possible answer: An estimate gives you an idea of what the answer should be so that you can place the decimal point.

Holt Mathematics

3-6 Dividing Decimals by Whole Numbers

1. Four friends go on a vacation together. They decide to share all expenses evenly. Estimate the cost of each item per person, and then compute the actual cost with a calculator.

Estimates may vary.

Item	Total Cost	Estimated Cost per Person	Actual Cost per Person
Cab fare	$50.00	$\frac{60}{4} = \$15$	$12.50
Pizza	$13.92	$\frac{12}{4} = \$3$	$3.48
Movie rental	$10.00	$\frac{8}{4} = \$2$	$2.50
Dinner	$76.20	$\frac{80}{4} = \$20$	$19.05
Boat ride	$35.96	$\frac{36}{4} = \$9$	$8.99

Estimate each quotient. Use this estimate to decide where to place a decimal point in the answer. Check with your calculator.

2. $125.2 \div 25 = 5.008$

3. $40 \div 16 = 2.5$

4. $7.5 \div 5 = 1.5$

5. $75 \div 12 = 6.25$

Think and Discuss

6. **Discuss** your strategies for estimating in number **1**. Possible answer: Round to a number easily divisible by 4.

7. **Explain** how you know where to place the decimal point in a quotient. Possible answer: An estimate gives you an idea of what the answer should be so that you can place the decimal point.

Holt Mathematics

3-7 Dividing by Decimals

A CD store carries the packages of recordable CDs listed in the table. The third column shows the cost of one CD for different packages. This is called the *unit cost.* The fourth column shows how many CDs one dollar can buy. For example, if you buy the 5-pack at $4.95, one dollar buys 1.01 CD (a little more than one CD). This is called the *purchasing power* of $1.00.

Use a calculator to find the cost of 1 CD and the purchasing power of $1.00 for each package.

	Item	Cost	Cost of 1 CD	Purchasing Power of $1.00
1.	Single CD	$1.19	$1.19 \div 1 = 1.19$	$1 \div 1.19 = 0.84$
2.	5-pack	$4.95	$4.95 \div 5 = 0.99$	$5 \div 4.95 = 1.01$
3.	10-pack	$8.95	$8.95 \div 10 = 0.90$	$10 \div 8.95 = 1.12$
4.	20-pack	$16.95	$16.95 \div 20 = 0.85$	$20 \div 16.95 = 1.18$
5.	50-pack	$35.95	$35.95 \div 50 = 0.72$	$50 \div 35.95 = 1.39$

6. Which package gives you the highest unit cost? single CD

7. Which package gives you the lowest unit cost? 50-pack

8. Which package gives you the greatest purchasing power per dollar? the least purchasing power per dollar?
50-pack; single CD

Think and Discuss

9. **Describe** the relationship between unit cost and purchasing power by looking at the numbers in the third and fourth columns above. Possible answer: The higher the unit cost, the lower the purchasing power.

Holt Mathematics

3-8 Interpret the Quotient

For each problem, estimate a solution. Then compute with a calculator. Estimates may vary.

		Estimate	Actual
1.	At Juan's school, each lunch special costs $3.65. How many lunches can Juan buy with $20.00?	$\frac{20}{4} = 5$	5
2.	Gasoline costs $2.499 per gallon. How many gallons can Sue buy with $25.00?	$\frac{25}{2.5} = 10$	10
3.	On Jorge's map, 0.15 cm represents 1 mi. He measures a road which is 7.8 cm. How many mi long is the actual road?	$\frac{7.5}{0.15} = 50$	52
4.	Ofelia makes $6.79 per hour at her summer job. If she wants to make $200 per week, how many hours should she work?	$\frac{210}{7} = 30$	29.5

Think and Discuss

5. **Explain** the estimation strategies you used. Possible answer: Round so that one number is easily divisible by the other.

6. **Describe** a problem that can be solved by division.

Possible answer: Mike saves $35 per week. How many weeks will it take him to save $700?

3-9 Solving Decimal Equations

For each equation, estimate the solution. Then use a calculator to solve the equation. Compare the calculated solution with your estimated solution. Estimates may vary.

		Estimate	Actual
1.	$1.25 + x = 10$	$x = 9$	$x = 8.75$
2.	$20 - x = 1.95$	$x = 18$	$x = 18.05$
3.	$6x = 15$	$x = 3$	$x = 2.5$
4.	$\dfrac{x}{4.5} = 10$	$x = 45$	$x = 45$
5.	$\dfrac{x}{100} = 1.609$	$x = 160$	$x = 160.9$

6. Write a real-world situation for the equation in Exercise **3.**
Possible answer: Patrick used 6 tiles to cover a distance of 15 inches. What is the length of each tile?

Think and Discuss

7. Explain which equations it was easiest to estimate a solution for. Possible answer: Exercises 4 and 5 were easiest because you could move the decimal point.

8. Describe a real-world situation that you could model with a decimal equation. Possible answer: Lana bought a book for $8.95 and paid with a $20 bill. How much change should she receive?

Holt Mathematics

4-1 Divisibility

Some calculators have an **INT ÷** key, which returns a quotient and a remainder.

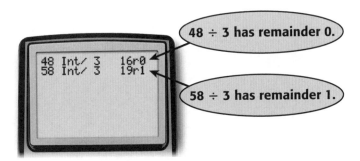

48 ÷ 3 has remainder 0.

58 ÷ 3 has remainder 1.

1. Use mental math or a calculator to determine each quotient and remainder. Then add the digits of the dividend.

	Dividend	Divisor	Quotient	Remainder	Sum of Digits
a.	48	3	16	0	$4 + 8 = 12$
b.	58	3	19	1	$5 + 8 = 13$
c.	256	3	85	1	$2+5+6=13$
d.	1,011	3	337	0	$1+0+1+1=3$
e.	72	3	24	0	$7 + 2 = 9$
f.	74	3	24	2	$7 + 4 = 11$
g.	129	3	43	0	$1+2+9=12$
h.	130	3	43	1	$1+3+0=4$

Think and Discuss

2. **Explain** whether 3,129 is divisible by 3. Yes; the sum of the digits is 15, which is divisible by 3.

3. **Describe** the pattern between the remainder and the sum of the digits in the table. Possible answer: If there is no remainder, the sum of the digits is divisible by 3. If there is a remainder, the remainder indicates how many units greater the number is than a number divisible by 3.

Holt Mathematics

4-2 Factors and Prime Factorization

1. The rectangle measures 4 units by 6 units and has an area of 24 square units. Use graph paper to draw rectangles that have different whole-number dimensions but still have an area of 24 square units. (*Hint:* $4 \times 6 = 24$. What factors other than 1×24 give you 24?)

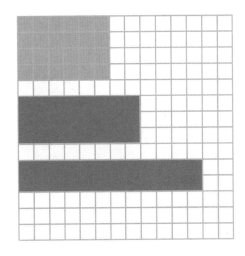

2. The rectangle measures 3 units by 5 units and has an area of 15 square units. Is it possible to draw rectangles that have whole-number dimensions other than 3×5 (and 1×15) and still have an area of 15 square units? no

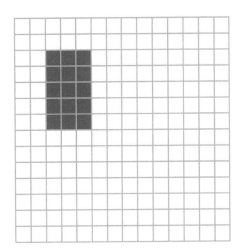

Think and Discuss

3. **Explain** how you can use rectangles to determine factors of numbers. Possible answer: The dimensions of the rectangle are the factors of the number.

4. **Explain** why it is possible to draw more than two different rectangles with an area of 24 square units, but it is not possible to draw more than two different rectangles with an area of 15 square units. Possible answer: 24 has more factors than 15.

Holt Mathematics

4-3 Greatest Common Factor

The sixth-grade band, which has 60 members, and the seventh-grade band, which has 48 members, are getting ready for a parade. How can they march together in blocks with the same number of columns? The model and table below show one possible formation.

1. Use graph paper to draw a model of two other formations that would work.

2. Complete the table to show the number of rows and columns in the other two formations.

	Formation 1		Formation 2		Formation 3	
	Rows	Columns	Rows	Columns	Rows	Columns
6th Grade	10	6	20	3	15	4
7th Grade	8	6	16	3	12	4

Think and Discuss

3. **Discuss** which formation the band director should select if she wants the bands to pass through the parade as quickly as possible. formation 1, because it has the fewest rows

4. **Explain** why both 48 and 60 must be divisible by the number of columns. Possible answer: This ensures that there are no incomplete rows or columns.

Holt Mathematics

4-4 Decimals and Fractions

Use the model to complete the table of equivalent fractions and decimals.

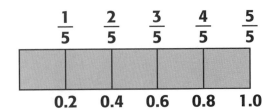

	Fraction	Decimal
1.	$\frac{1}{5}$	0.2
2.	$\frac{3}{5}$	0.6
3.	$\frac{2}{5}$	0.4
4.	$\frac{4}{5}$	0.8

Use the model to complete the table of equivalent fractions and decimals.

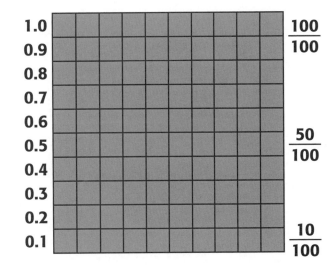

	Fraction	Decimal
5.	$\frac{10}{100}$	0.1
6.	$\frac{45}{100}$	0.45
7.	$\frac{40}{100}$	0.4
8.	$\frac{30}{100}$	0.30

Think and Discuss

9. Describe a situation in which decimals are used. Possible answer: money

10. Describe a situation in which fractions are used.

Possible answer: recipes

Holt Mathematics

4-5 Equivalent Fractions

Equivalent fractions are fractions that have the same value.

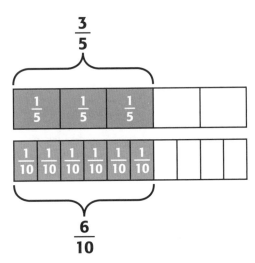

Use the models below to find equivalent fractions.

1. $\frac{1}{2} = \boxed{\frac{2}{4}} = \boxed{\frac{3}{6}} = \boxed{\frac{4}{8}}$

2. $\frac{2}{3} = \boxed{\frac{4}{6}} = \boxed{\frac{8}{12}}$

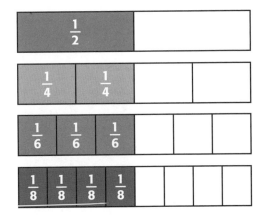

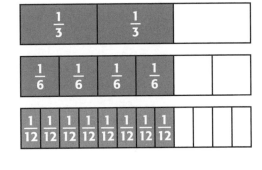

Think and Discuss

3. **Describe** how you could write $\frac{1}{2}$ as an equivalent fraction with a denominator of 24. Possible answer: $\frac{12}{24}$, because the numerator must be half the denominator

4. **Discuss** whether $\frac{6}{12}$ and $\frac{9}{18}$ are equivalent fractions.

   Possible answer: They are both equivalent to $\frac{1}{2}$.

Holt Mathematics

4-6 Mixed Numbers and Improper Fractions

An *improper fraction* is a fraction in which the numerator is greater than or equal to the denominator. The model shows that $\frac{7}{4} = \frac{4}{4} + \frac{3}{4} = 1 + \frac{3}{4}$.

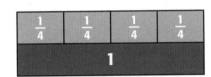

The mixed number $1\frac{3}{4} = 1 + \frac{3}{4}$.

For each improper fraction, complete the model and write the improper fraction as a mixed number.

1. $\frac{5}{3}$ 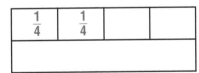 $\underline{\hspace{1cm} 1\frac{2}{3} \hspace{1cm}}$

2. $\frac{7}{6}$ 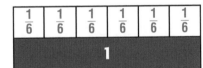 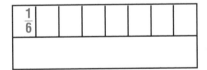 $\underline{\hspace{1cm} 1\frac{1}{6} \hspace{1cm}}$

3. $\frac{6}{4}$ 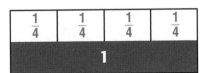 $\underline{\hspace{1cm} 1\frac{1}{2} \hspace{1cm}}$

Think and Discuss

4. **Explain** why $\frac{6}{4} = 1\frac{1}{2}$. **Possible answer:** $\frac{6}{4} = \frac{4}{4} + \frac{2}{4}$; $\frac{4}{4} = 1$ and $\frac{2}{4} = \frac{1}{2}$, so $\frac{6}{4} = 1\frac{1}{2}$.

5. **Discuss** a situation in which mixed numbers are used.

   Possible answer: measuring snow or rainfall amounts

Holt Mathematics

4-7 Comparing and Ordering Fractions

Use the model to decide whether the fraction on the left is greater than (>), less than (<), or equal to (=) the fraction on the right.

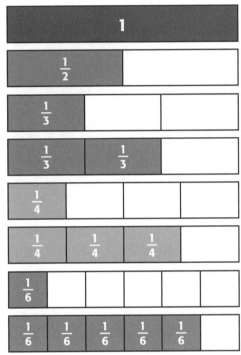

1. $\frac{1}{2}$ $\boxed{>}$ $\frac{1}{3}$

2. $\frac{1}{2}$ $\boxed{>}$ $\frac{1}{4}$

3. $\frac{1}{2}$ $\boxed{<}$ $\frac{2}{3}$

4. $\frac{1}{3}$ $\boxed{>}$ $\frac{1}{4}$

5. $\frac{3}{4}$ $\boxed{>}$ $\frac{2}{3}$

6. $\frac{3}{4}$ $\boxed{<}$ $\frac{5}{6}$

7. $\frac{1}{6}$ $\boxed{<}$ $\frac{1}{4}$

8. Look at the calculator screen to compare $\frac{1}{2}$ and $\frac{2}{3}$. Which fraction is greater? How do you know? $\frac{2}{3} > \frac{1}{2}$ because $0.\overline{6} > 0.5$.

Think and Discuss

9. **Explain** how you could compare a fraction and a decimal.

10. **Explain** why $\frac{1}{17}$ is greater than $\frac{1}{18}$.

9. Possible answer: Write the fraction as a decimal or the decimal as a fraction.

10. Possible answer: 1 out of 17 equal parts is more than 1 out of 18 equal parts.

Holt Mathematics

4-8 Adding and Subtracting with Like Denominators

Suzanne runs on a $\frac{3}{4}$-mile track. She ran one lap and then decided to run one more lap.

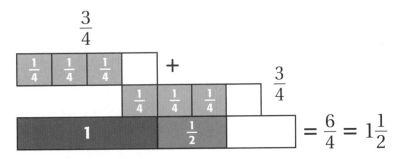

Susan ran $1\frac{1}{2}$ miles.

Draw a model to solve each addition problem.

1. $\frac{3}{5} + \frac{4}{5}$ $1\frac{2}{5}$

2. $\frac{3}{10} + \frac{7}{10}$ 1

Paul is recording a CD and has $\frac{1}{6}$ of the work completed. How much recording is left?

Paul needs to record $\frac{5}{6}$ of the CD.

$$1 - \frac{1}{6} = \frac{6}{6} - \frac{1}{6} = \frac{5}{6}$$

Draw a model to solve each subtraction problem.

3. $\frac{4}{5} - \frac{3}{5}$ $\frac{1}{5}$ $\frac{4}{5} - \frac{3}{5} = \frac{1}{5}$

4. $1 - \frac{3}{10}$ $\frac{7}{10}$ $1 - \frac{3}{10} = \frac{7}{10}$

Think and Discuss

5. Explain how to add and subtract fractions with like denominators. Possible answer: Add or subtract the numerators, and keep the denominator the same.

6. Explain how to subtract a fraction from 1. Possible answer: Write 1 as a fraction with the same denominator as the fraction being subtracted. Then subtract the numerators.

Holt Mathematics

4-9 Estimating Fraction Sums and Differences

Out of 80 students, 49 are in athletics. As the number lines show, approximately half the students are in athletics. In other words, $\frac{49}{80}$ is close to $\frac{1}{2}$.

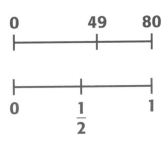

Use a number line to determine whether each fraction is closest to 0, $\frac{1}{2}$, or 1.

1. $\frac{79}{99}$ 1

2. $\frac{22}{213}$ 0

3. $\frac{15}{27}$ $\frac{1}{2}$

4. $\frac{22}{45}$ $\frac{1}{2}$

5. $\frac{300}{475}$ $\frac{1}{2}$

6. $\frac{400}{475}$ 1

Use the estimates you found in numbers 1–6 to estimate each sum or difference.

7. $\frac{79}{99} + \frac{15}{27}$ $1\frac{1}{2}$

8. $\frac{22}{213} + \frac{22}{45}$ $\frac{1}{2}$

9. $\frac{300}{475} - \frac{22}{45}$ 0

10. $\frac{15}{27} - \frac{22}{45}$ 0

Think and Discuss

11. **Discuss** your strategies for determining whether the fractions were closest to 0, $\frac{1}{2}$, or 1.

12. **Explain** how you know $\frac{237}{475}$ is less than $\frac{1}{2}$.

11. Possible answer: If the numerator is about $\frac{1}{2}$ the denominator, the fraction is close to $\frac{1}{2}$. If the numerator is much less than $\frac{1}{2}$ the denominator, the fraction is close to 0. If the numerator is much more than $\frac{1}{2}$ the denominator, the fraction is close to 1.

12. Possible answer: 237 is less than half of 475, so the fraction is less than $\frac{1}{2}$.

Holt Mathematics

EXPLORATION

5-1 Least Common Multiple

1. Sarah and Jane enter a walkathon for charity. They start together, but Sarah completes one lap every 6 minutes while Jane completes one lap every 8 minutes.

Number of Laps Completed	Sarah's Time (min)	Jane's Time (min)
1	$6 \cdot 1 = 6$	$8 \cdot 1 = 8$
2	$6 \cdot 2 = 12$	$8 \cdot 2 = 16$
3	$6 \cdot 3 = 18$	$8 \cdot 3 = 24$
4	$6 \cdot 4 = 24$	$8 \cdot 4 = 32$
5	$6 \cdot 5 = 30$	$8 \cdot 5 = 40$
6	$6 \cdot 6 = 36$	$8 \cdot 6 = 48$
7	$6 \cdot 7 = 42$	$8 \cdot 7 = 56$
8	$6 \cdot 8 = 48$	$8 \cdot 8 = 64$

a. After how many minutes will Sarah and Jane meet at the start again? 24 minutes

b. When will they meet the next time? 48 minutes

Think and Discuss

2. **Discuss** the solution to number **1a** using the term *common multiple.* Possible answer: 24 is a common multiple of 6 and 8.

3. **Compare** the solution to number **1a** with the solution to number **1b,** and describe these solutions using the terms *common multiple* and *least common multiple.* Possible answer: 48 is a common multiple of 6 and 8, but 24 is the least common multiple of 6 and 8.

Holt Mathematics

5-2 Adding and Subtracting with Unlike Denominators

Fractions are pieces of a whole. When you add or subtract fractions with unlike denominators, you are usually adding or subtracting pieces of different sizes. Look at the model used to solve the problem below.

Phil combines $\frac{1}{4}$ gallon of paint with $\frac{1}{2}$ gallon of paint. How much paint does he have now?

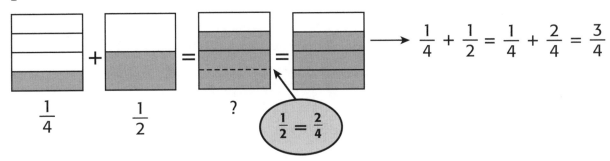

$$\frac{1}{4} + \frac{1}{2} = \frac{1}{4} + \frac{2}{4} = \frac{3}{4}$$

$$\frac{1}{2} = \frac{2}{4}$$

Phil has $\frac{3}{4}$ gallon of paint.

1. Draw a model to show that $1 - \frac{1}{4} = \frac{3}{4}$.

Draw a model to solve each problem. Simplify your answers.

2. $\frac{1}{2} + \frac{1}{3}$ $\frac{5}{6}$

3. $\frac{4}{5} - \frac{1}{2}$ $\frac{3}{10}$

Think and Discuss

4. **Explain** how to add and subtract fractions with unlike denominators. Find a common denominator.

5. **Draw** a model to show $\frac{1}{2} + \frac{2}{3} = 1\frac{1}{6}$.

$$\frac{3}{6} + \frac{4}{6} = \frac{7}{6}$$

Holt Mathematics

5-3 Adding and Subtracting Mixed Numbers

The graph shows typical rainfall levels for a city in the Southwest for the first 5 months of the year. What is the approximate total rainfall from January through May?

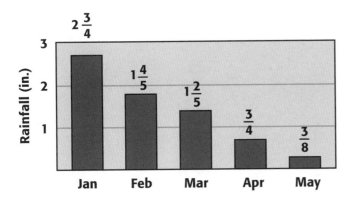

A mixed number contains a whole number and a fraction. To estimate with mixed numbers, round each mixed number to the nearest whole number.

Actual $\quad 2\frac{3}{4} + 1\frac{4}{5} + 1\frac{2}{5} + \frac{3}{4} + \frac{3}{8}$

$\qquad\qquad \downarrow \quad\; \downarrow \quad\; \downarrow \quad\; \downarrow \quad\; \downarrow$

Estimated $\quad 3 \;+\; 2 \;+\; 1 \;+\; 1 \;+\; 0 = 7$ in.

The total rainfall is about 7 inches.

Estimate each sum or difference.

1. $13\frac{1}{2} - 9\frac{27}{32}$ $14 - 10 = 4$

2. $1\frac{1}{2} + 9\frac{3}{8} - 2\frac{1}{4}$ $2 + 9 - 2 = 9$

3. $17\frac{7}{8} + 19\frac{1}{10}$ $18 + 19 = 37$

4. $4\frac{1}{8} - 1\frac{3}{10} + 3\frac{1}{4}$ $4 - 1 + 3 = 6$

Think and Discuss

5. Discuss the estimation strategies you used. Possible answer: Round fractions to the nearest whole number and then add or subtract.

6. Describe a real-world situation in which mixed numbers are added or subtracted. Possible answer: measuring lengths of wood; combining ingredients in a recipe

Holt Mathematics

5-4 Regrouping to Subtract Mixed Numbers

A baker starts the day with $2\frac{1}{4}$ lemon cakes and sells $1\frac{1}{2}$ lemon cakes during the day. How much cake is left over?

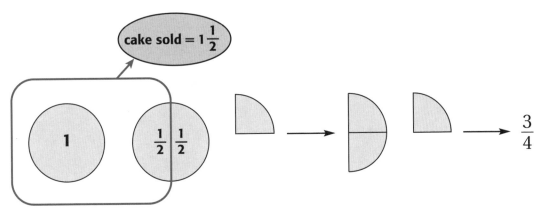

initial amount of cake $= 2\frac{1}{4}$ cake left $= \frac{3}{4}$

There is $\frac{3}{4}$ of a cake left over.

Use a model to solve each subtraction problem.

1. $2 - 1\frac{1}{4}$ $\frac{3}{4}$ **2.** $4 - 1\frac{1}{2}$ $2\frac{1}{2}$

3. $5\frac{1}{4} - 3\frac{1}{2}$ $1\frac{3}{4}$ **4.** $1\frac{1}{8} - \frac{3}{4}$ $\frac{3}{8}$

Think and Discuss

5. Discuss your method for subtracting mixed numbers.

6. Explain why the method used to solve the problem about the lemon cakes is called regrouping.

5. Possible answer: Regroup the first fraction by changing one of its wholes into a fraction equal to 1.

6. Possible answer: The whole number is regrouped into a whole number plus a fraction equal to 1.

Holt Mathematics

5-5 Solving Fraction Equations: Addition and Subtraction

You can use mental math to solve addition and subtraction equations that contain fractions. Look at the reasoning used to solve $\frac{7}{9} - x = \frac{2}{9}$.

Since the denominators of the fractions are the same, you can rewrite $\frac{7}{9} - x = \frac{2}{9}$ as a simpler equation: $7 - \blacksquare = 2$.

$7 - \blacksquare = 2$	*Think:* 7 minus what number equals 2?
$7 - \boxed{5} = 2$	Use mental math.
$\frac{7}{9} - \frac{5}{9} = \frac{2}{9}$	Write the equation, using the denominator.
$x = \frac{5}{9}$	Write the value of x.

Using the example above as a guide, complete the table below.

	Equation	Simpler Equation	Value of x
1.	$\frac{1}{2} + x = \frac{7}{2}$	$1 + \blacksquare = 7$	$\frac{6}{2} = 3$
2.	$x - \frac{2}{5} = \frac{1}{5}$	$\blacksquare - 2 = 1$	$\frac{3}{5}$
3.	$x + \frac{1}{3} = \frac{2}{3}$	$\blacksquare + 1 = 2$	$\frac{1}{3}$
4.	$x - \frac{1}{3} = \frac{2}{3}$	$\blacksquare - 1 = 2$	$\frac{3}{3} = 1$

Think and Discuss

5. Explain how you could use mental math to solve the equation $\frac{1}{3} + x = \frac{5}{6}$. **Possible answer: Use $\frac{2}{6}$ for $\frac{1}{3}$. Then solve the simpler equation $2 + \square = 5$ to see that $x = \frac{3}{6}$ or $\frac{1}{2}$.**

Holt Mathematics

EXPLORATION

5-6 Multiplying Fractions by Whole Numbers

Rosario requires $\frac{3}{4}$ of a 1-pound bag of clay to make one bowl. How many 1-pound bags of clay will she need to make a set of 6 bowls?

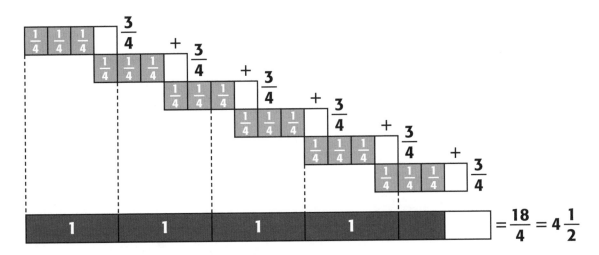

She will need $4\frac{1}{2}$ 1-pound bags of clay.

Draw a model to find each product.

1. $3 \cdot \frac{3}{4}$

2. $4 \cdot \frac{1}{2}$

3. $5 \cdot \frac{2}{3}$

4. $7 \cdot \frac{1}{4}$

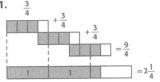

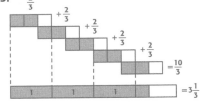

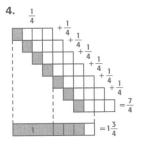

Think and Discuss

5. Explain how you know that $3 \cdot \frac{3}{4}$ is less than 3.

Possible answer: $\frac{3}{4}$ is less than 1, so $3 \cdot \frac{3}{4} < 3 \cdot 1 = 3$.

Holt Mathematics

EXPLORATION

5-7 Multiplying Fractions

You can use paper folding to find the product of two fractions. To find $\frac{3}{4}$ of $\frac{1}{2}$, fold the paper in half vertically to model $\frac{1}{2}$. Then fold it horizontally into four sections to create fourths.

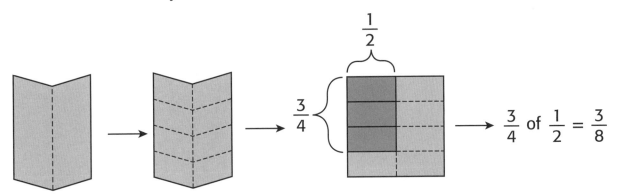

Use paper folding to find each product. Sketch a picture for each product.

1. $\frac{1}{2} \cdot \frac{1}{2}$

2. $\frac{1}{2} \cdot \frac{2}{3}$

3. $\frac{1}{3} \cdot \frac{1}{4}$

4. $\frac{2}{3} \cdot \frac{3}{4}$

Think and Discuss

5. Explain how to multiply two fractions. Possible answer: Multiply the numerators and multiply the denominators.

Holt Mathematics

5-8 Multiplying Mixed Numbers

You can use paper folding to find products of mixed numbers. To find $\frac{1}{2} \cdot 1\frac{1}{2}$, first fold two sheets of paper in half vertically to represent $1\frac{1}{2}$. To represent $\frac{1}{2}$ of $1\frac{1}{2}$, fold both sheets in half again horizontally.

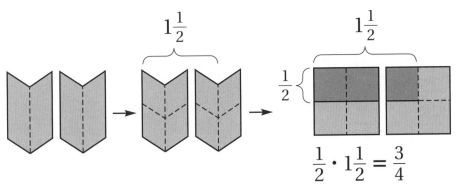

$$\frac{1}{2} \cdot 1\frac{1}{2} = \frac{3}{4}$$

Use paper folding to find each product. Sketch a picture for each product.

1. $\frac{2}{3} \cdot 1\frac{1}{2}$

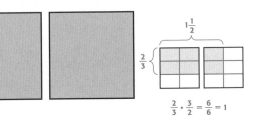

$$\frac{2}{3} \cdot \frac{3}{2} = \frac{6}{6} = 1$$

2. $\frac{1}{3} \cdot 1\frac{3}{4}$

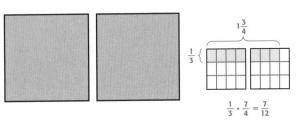

$$\frac{1}{3} \cdot \frac{7}{4} = \frac{7}{12}$$

Think and Discuss

3. Explain how to multiply a fraction times a mixed number.

4. Explain why the product of a proper fraction and a mixed number is less than the mixed number.

3. Possible answer: Change the mixed number to an improper fraction and multiply.

4. Possible answer: The product is less than the mixed number because you are multiplying it by a number less than 1.

Holt Mathematics

5-9 Dividing Fractions and Mixed Numbers

The model shows the quotient $2\frac{1}{2} \div \frac{1}{2}$.

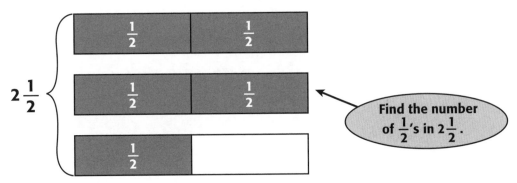

Find the number of $\frac{1}{2}$'s in $2\frac{1}{2}$.

There are 5 halves in $2\frac{1}{2}$, so $2\frac{1}{2} \div \frac{1}{2} = 5$.

Draw a model to solve each division problem.

1. $1\frac{1}{2} \div \frac{3}{4}$ 2

2. $2 \div \frac{2}{3}$ 3

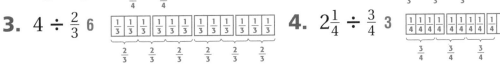 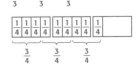

3. $4 \div \frac{2}{3}$ 6

4. $2\frac{1}{4} \div \frac{3}{4}$ 3

Think and Discuss

5. Describe how to model fraction division by using fraction bars.

6. Explain why $3 \div \frac{3}{4} = 4$.

5. Possible answer: Using the denominator of the divisor as the unit of the fraction bars, represent the dividend. Then put the bars into groups as indicated by the numerator of the divisor.

6. $3 = \frac{12}{4}$ and $\frac{12}{4}$ contains 4 groups of $\frac{3}{4}$, so $3 \div \frac{3}{4} = 4$.

Holt Mathematics

5-10 Solving Fraction Equations: Multiplication and Division

You can use a number line to solve fraction equations. Look at the reasoning used to solve the equation $\frac{1}{2}n = 50$.

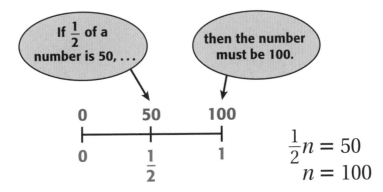

If $\frac{1}{2}$ of a number is 50, ...

then the number must be 100.

$$\frac{1}{2}n = 50$$
$$n = 100$$

Complete the number line to solve each equation.

1. $\frac{1}{2}n = 125$

   $n = 250$

2. $\frac{1}{3}n = 12$

   $n = 36$

3. $\frac{3}{4}n = 60$

   $n = 80$

4. $\frac{2}{3}n = 20$

   $n = 30$

Think and Discuss

5. **Describe** a real-world situation that could be represented by the equation in number **3**.

6. **Discuss** another way of solving equations that contain fractions and involve multiplication.

5. Possible answer: Sixty people represent $\frac{3}{4}$ of the capacity of a dance hall.

6. Possible answer: Multiply both sides of the equation by the reciprocal of the fraction.

Holt Mathematics

6-1 Make a Table

The table shows the number of medals awarded to the top 13 medal-winning countries during the 2002 Winter Olympics.

1. Compute the total number of medals won by each country.

Country	Gold	Silver	Bronze	Total
Germany	12	16	7	35
USA	10	13	11	34
Norway	11	7	6	24
Canada	6	3	8	17
Austria	2	4	10	16
Russia	6	6	4	16
Italy	4	4	4	12
France	4	5	2	11
Switzerland	3	2	6	11
China	2	2	4	8
Netherlands	3	5	0	8
Finland	4	2	1	7
Sweden	0	2	4	6

Think and Discuss

2. Explain why the table is set up the way it is.

3. Describe a different way to organize this data.

2. Possible answer: The countries are listed in descending order based on the total number of medals won.

3. Possible answer: The countries could be listed in alphabetical order.

Holt Mathematics

6-2 Mean, Median, Mode, and Range

The table shows an ordered list of all the times in the men's 1,500-meter speed-skating competition in the 2002 Winter Olympics. The fastest time was 1:43.95, or 1 minute 43.95 seconds. Notice that all of the times are only seconds apart.

1:43.95	1:44.57	1:45.26	1:45.34	1:45.41	1:45.51	1:45.63	1:45.82
1:45.86	1:45.97	1:45.98	1:46.00	1:46.04	1:46.29	1:46.38	1:46.40
1:46.75	1:46.99	1:47.04	1:47.21	1:47.26	1:47.63	1:47.64	1:47.72
1:47.78	1:47.83	1:48.02	1:48.13	1:48.20	1:48.27	1:48.40	1:48.57
1:48.58	1:48.76	1:49.24	1:49.42	1:49.45	1:49.50	1:49.57	1:50.15
1:50.26	1:50.70	1:51.02	1:51.02	1:51.81	1:52.01	1:52.87	

1. How many seconds behind the winner was the second-place skater? the third-place skater? 0.62 s, 1.31 s

2. Find the range. (Subtract the fastest time from the slowest time.) 8.92 s

3. Find the median. (The median is the number in the middle of the data set.) 1:47.72 s

4. Find the mean. (The mean is the average of all the times.) 1:47.83 s

Think and Discuss

5. **Discuss** how you found the median. Possible answer: There are 47 values in the table, so the median will be the 24th value.

6. **Explain** how the mean compares with the median.
   Possible answer: The mean is slightly greater than the median.

Holt Mathematics

6-3 Additional Data and Outliers

Casey Fitzrandolph won the men's 500-meter speed-skating competition in the 2002 Olympics with a time of **69.23 seconds.** The table lists the top 32 times in the 500-meter race.

69.23	69.26	69.47	69.49	69.59	69.60	69.60	69.81
69.86	69.89	70.10	70.11	70.28	70.32	70.33	70.44
70.57	70.75	70.84	70.88	70.97	71.27	71.39	71.54
71.96	72.07	72.49	72.58	72.64	72.69	72.93	74.81

1. Find the range, which is the difference between the fastest and the slowest time. 5.58 s

2. Find the median, which is the number in the middle of the data set. 70.505 s

3. Find the mean with a calculator. 70.8675 s

4. The table excluded three more times. These times are 108.46, 117.41, and 133.57. Calculate the range, median, and mean including these three additional times. 64.34 s; 70.75 s; 75.0629 s

Think and Discuss

5. **Discuss** why the last three times in number 4 were excluded from the table above. Possible answer: These values are much greater than all the other values in the table.

6. **Describe** how the additional three times affect the range, median, and mean. The range and the mean increase significantly. The median is barely affected.

Holt Mathematics

6-4 Bar Graphs

The bar graph shows the medal totals of the four countries that won the most medals at the 2002 Winter Olympic Games.

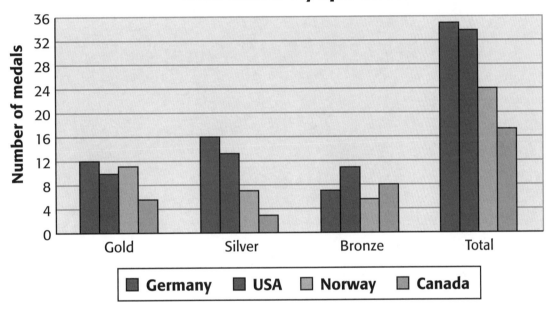

Top Four Medal-Winning Countries at 2002 Winter Olympic Games

■ Germany   ■ USA   □ Norway   ■ Canada

1. Name the country that won

   a. the most gold medals. Germany

   b. the most silver medals. Germany

   c. the most bronze medals. USA

   d. the most medals overall. Germany

2. What is the total number of medals won by each country?
   Germany: 35; USA: 34; Norway: 24; Canada: 17

Think and Discuss

3. **Explain** a different way to display the data.
   Possible answer: The graph could be reorganized so the bars are horizontal.

4. **Discuss** information that is not shown by the bar graph.
   Possible answer: the number of medals won by other countries

Holt Mathematics

6-5 Line Plots, Frequency Tables, and Histograms

Below are the top 50 women's times at the 2002 Olympic biathlon.

20:41.4	20:57.0	21:20.4	21:24.1	21:27.9	21:32.1	21:35.7	21:44.2
21:50.3	21:55.6	21:57.0	22:01.7	22:11.9	22:14.9	22:17.7	22:19.7
22:20.6	22:25.8	22:27.3	22:29.9	22:32.1	22:33.5	22:37.7	22:39.9
22:41.1	22:44.7	22:45.5	22:58.3	23:00.0	23:03.5	23:03.8	23:05.0
23:06.6	23:09.4	23:10.0	23:11.2	23:11.3	23:14.2	23:14.6	23:14.7
23:18.0	23:18.9	23:24.6	23:26.5	23:36.8	23:36.9	23:37.4	23:40.9
23:44.1	23:48.7						

1. Complete the *frequency table.*

Time (min)	20:00.0–20:59.9	21:00.0–21:59.9	22:00.0–22:59.9	23:00.0–23:59.9
Frequency	2	9	17	22

2. Use the numbers in the frequency table to complete the *histogram.*

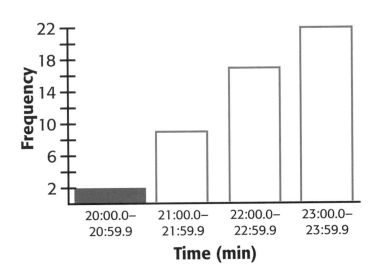

Think and Discuss

3. Explain how you completed the histogram in number **2.**

Possible answer: For each range of times, draw a bar with a height that matches the frequency in the table.

Holt Mathematics

6-6 Ordered Pairs

The table shows the number of faces and vertices of the five regular polyhedrons.

Faces	4	8	20	6	12
Vertices	4	6	12	8	20

This data can be represented on a graph using **ordered pairs.** Each ordered pair is composed of the number of faces and the number of vertices of the polyhedron.

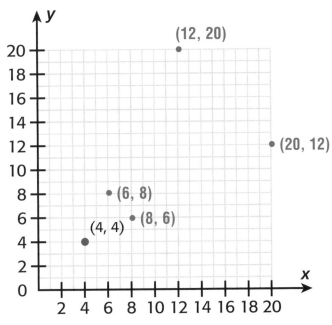

1. Plot and label the remaining ordered pairs. First find the number of faces on the horizontal line. From the number of faces, move up to find the number of vertices on the vertical line.

Think and Discuss

2. **Explain** how to plot ordered pairs. Possible answer: Use the first number to move along the x-axis and the second number to move up parallel to the y-axis.

3. **Discuss** what the point (6, 8) means. Possible answer: The point is 6 units to the right of the x-axis and then 8 units up.

Holt Mathematics

6-7 Line Graphs

Luis works at a record store. His manager asked him to graph the number of CDs returned each day during one week.

Day	Sun	Mon	Tue	Wed	Thu	Fri	Sat
CDs Returned	10	3	2	4	7	11	14

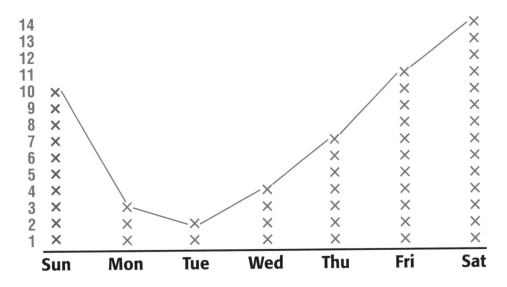

1. Complete the line plot.

2. Draw a vertical line to the left of Sun (Sunday) to form the y-axis. Number this line from 1 to 14.

3. Delete all the ×'s in each stack except the one at the top.

4. Connect the ×'s with line segments. You have constructed a *line graph.*

Think and Discuss

5. **Explain** how to construct a line graph. Possible answer: Draw and label horizontal and vertical axes. Plot points and connect.

6. **Discuss** some advantages of displaying data on a line graph rather than in a table. Possible answer: A line graph makes it easier to compare values and recognize trends.

Holt Mathematics

6-8 Misleading Graphs

The graph shows the total number of medals won by four countries at the 2002 Winter Olympics.

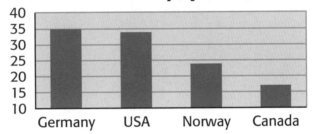

Top Four Medal-Winning Countries at 2002 Winter Olympic Games

1. According to the height of each bar, which country appears to have won approximately half the number of medals won by the United States? Norway

2. Look at the numbers on the left to estimate the number of medals won by each country. Germany: 35; USA: 34; Norway: 24; Canada: 17

3. Use the estimates in number **2** to determine whether the answer to number **1** is accurate. No

Think and Discuss

4. **Discuss** why the graph is misleading. The vertical axis starts at 10 rather than 0.

5. **Explain** how you could modify the graph to represent the data more accurately. Possible answer: Start the vertical axis at 0.

Holt Mathematics

6-9 Stem-and-Leaf Plots

The table shows the times in seconds and hundredths of seconds for the women's 500-meter speed-skating competition in the 2002 Winter Olympics.

74.75	74.94	75.19	75.37	75.39	75.64	75.64	76.17	76.20	76.31
76.37	76.42	76.62	76.73	76.73	76.86	76.92	77.10	77.37	77.60
77.60	77.71	78.26	78.63	78.79	78.89	79.28	79.45	79.45	

You can organize the data by seconds and hundredths of seconds. Notice how the times are grouped using different colors.

1. Complete the *stem-and-leaf plot.* The stems represent seconds and the leaves represent hundredths of seconds. Notice how the colors correspond to the colors used in the table.

Stems	Leaves
74	75 94
75	19 37 39 64 64
76	17 20 31 37 42 62 73 73 86 92
77	10 37 60 60 71
78	26 63 79 89
79	28 45 45

Key: 74 | 75 means 74.75

Think and Discuss

2. **Explain** what it means in this case for a stem to have the most number of leaves. The greatest number of skaters finished in that many seconds.

3. **Explain** what it means in this case for a stem to have the least number of leaves. The least number of skaters finished in that many seconds.

Holt Mathematics

6-10 Choosing an Appropriate Display

The graphs shown below are not labeled. Match each of the descriptions with the graph that most likely represents the data.

1. The population of a town over the course of several years
Graph C

2. The areas of the five Great Lakes *Graph A*

3. The test scores of the students in a Spanish class *Graph B*

Graph A

Graph B

Stems	Leaves
6	3 4 7
7	5 5 5 8
8	2 3 5 7 9 9
9	1 4 8

Key: 6 | 3 means 63

Graph C

Think and Discuss

4. Explain how you decided which graph matches each description.

5. Explain what you would need to do to complete Graph A.

4. Possible answer: A population over time is best shown with a line graph; the data about the areas of the lakes is best shown in a bar graph, and test scores can be shown in a stem-and-leaf plot.

5. Add the names of the lakes on the vertical axis; add the areas along the horizontal axis, and give the graph a title.

Holt Mathematics

7-1 Ratios and Rates

A TV network offers the numbers of shows each week shown in the table.

You can compare the numbers of TV shows by using ratios. A *ratio* is a comparison of two quantities that uses division. For example, the ratio of science fiction shows to drama shows is $\frac{3}{14}$, which can also be written 3:14 or 3 to 14.

Type of TV Show	Number of Shows
Comedy	14
Drama	14
Science fiction	3
Game show	7
Talk show	15
News	14
Morning show	10
Late-night show	5
Sports	6

Find each ratio.

1. comedy shows to game shows 14:7 or 2:1

2. game shows to news shows 7:14 or 1:2

3. morning shows to late-night shows 10:5 or 2:1

4. talk shows to sports shows 15:6 or 5:2

Think and Discuss

5. **Discuss** whether the ratios in numbers 1−4 compare part to part, part to whole, or whole to part. part to part

6. **Discuss** whether order is important when calculating ratios. (*Hint:* Is $\frac{news}{sports}$ equivalent to $\frac{sports}{news}$?) Yes, order is important.

Holt Mathematics

7-2 Using Tables to Explore Equivalent Ratios and Rates

McMillans Restaurant is celebrating its 50th anniversary by offering 3 hamburgers for $2.

1. Sue makes this table for quick reference at the drive-up window. Complete the table.

Number of Hamburgers	3	6	9	12	15	18	21
Total Cost ($)	2	4	6	8	10	12	14

2. The weekend goal is to sell 1,200 hamburgers. How much money will the restaurant receive if it reaches its goal of 1,200 hamburgers? Complete the table to help you answer this question. $800

Number of Hamburgers Sold	300	600	900	1,200
Amount Received ($)	200	400	600	800

Think and Discuss

3. **Describe** any patterns you notice in the table for Exercise 1.

4. **Explain** how you could find the amount of money the restaurant would receive if it sold 1,500 hamburgers.

3. Possible answer: The number of hamburgers increases by 3 while the total cost increases by 2. In each column, the total cost is always $\frac{2}{3}$ the number of hamburgers.

4. Possible answer: Extend the table. For 1,500 hamburgers, the amount received would be $1,000.

Holt Mathematics

7-3 Proportions

An automobile assembly line finishes 3 cars every 2 hours.

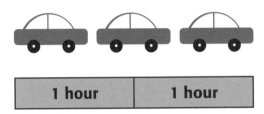

| 1 hour | 1 hour |

1. Use the diagram to determine how many cars are finished each hour. $1\frac{1}{2}$

2. Use the diagram to determine approximately how long it takes to finish 1 car. $\frac{2}{3}$ h

3. If it takes 2 hours to finish 3 cars, how many hours does it take to finish
   a. 6 cars? 4 h   b. 9 cars? 6 h   c. 12 cars? 8 h
   d. 4 cars? $2\frac{2}{3}$ h   e. 8 cars? $5\frac{1}{3}$ h   f. 16 cars? $10\frac{2}{3}$ h

Think and Discuss

4. **Discuss** how you used the diagram to solve numbers 1 and 2. Possible answer Use one hour bar to estimate how many cars it takes to equal one bar. Use one car to estimate how much of one hour equals one car.

5. **Explain** how you solved numbers 3a−3f.
   Possible answer: Extend the diagram.

Holt Mathematics

7-4 Similar Figures

Similar rectangles have the same shape but may be different sizes.

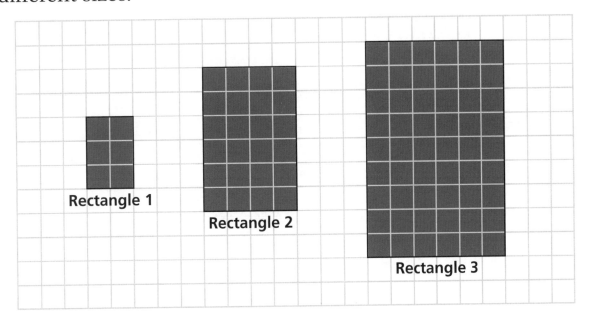

Rectangle 1

Rectangle 2

Rectangle 3

Determine the length and width of each rectangle and find each ratio.

Ratio 1		Ratio 2	
1.	$\dfrac{\text{length of rectangle 1}}{\text{length of rectangle 2}} = \dfrac{3}{6} = \dfrac{1}{2}$	$\dfrac{\text{width of rectangle 1}}{\text{width of rectangle 2}} = \dfrac{2}{4} = \dfrac{1}{2}$	
2.	$\dfrac{\text{length of rectangle 2}}{\text{length of rectangle 3}} = \dfrac{6}{9} = \dfrac{2}{3}$	$\dfrac{\text{width of rectangle 2}}{\text{width of rectangle 3}} = \dfrac{4}{6} = \dfrac{2}{3}$	
3.	$\dfrac{\text{length of rectangle 1}}{\text{length of rectangle 3}} = \dfrac{3}{9} = \dfrac{1}{3}$	$\dfrac{\text{width of rectangle 1}}{\text{width of rectangle 3}} = \dfrac{2}{6} = \dfrac{1}{3}$	

Think and Discuss

Possible answer: The ratios are

4. Describe the pattern between ratio 1 and ratio 2. equivalent.

5. Explain why the three rectangles are similar. Possible answer:
They all have the same shape.

Holt Mathematics

7-5 Indirect Measurement

The heights of very tall structures can be measured indirectly using similar figures and proportions. This method is called *indirect measurement.*

Augustine and Carmen want to measure the height of the school's flagpole. To do this, they go outside and hold a meterstick upright. The meterstick casts a shadow that measures 50 cm.

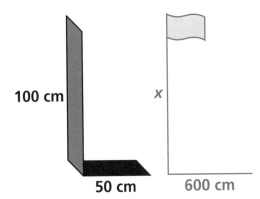

100 cm
50 cm
x
600 cm

1. If the shadow of the flagpole measures 6 meters, how tall is the flagpole? To answer this question, follow these steps:

   a. Draw a sketch of the flagpole and its shadow next to the sketch of the meterstick and its shadow.

   b. Label the height of the flagpole x.

   c. Write the proportion $\frac{\text{height of flagpole}}{\text{shadow of flagpole}} = \frac{\text{height of meterstick}}{\text{shadow of meterstick}}$, and substitute the values for the given measurements. $\frac{x}{600} = \frac{100}{50}$

   d. Solve the proportion for x. 1,200 cm or 12 m

Think and Discuss

2. **Explain** how you solved the proportion for x in number **1d.**

3. **Explain** whether you could have solved the problem by writing the proportion as $\frac{\text{shadow of flagpole}}{\text{height of flagpole}} = \frac{\text{shadow of meterstick}}{\text{height of meterstick}}$.

2. Possible answer: Set the cross products equal to each other.

3. Possible answer: Yes, it is an equivalent proportion.

Holt Mathematics

7-6 Scale Drawings and Maps

A *scale* is a ratio between two sets of measurements. For example, the scale 2 in:1 mi means that 2 inches on a scale drawing represents 1 mile.

1. Each letter of the Hollywood sign measures 50 ft tall and 30 ft wide. Use the rectangles below to sketch a scale drawing of the Hollywood sign. The side lengths of each square inside each rectangle represent 10 ft.

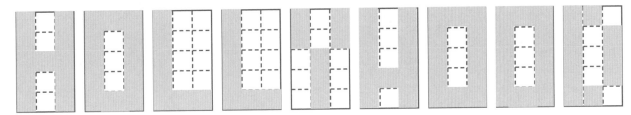

2. If the total width of the Hollywood sign is approximately 450 ft, what is the approximate distance between each pair of neighboring letters? 22.5 ft

Think and Discuss

3. **Explain** how you found the answer in number 2.
4. **Discuss** other examples of scale drawings.

3. Possible answer: The total length of the letters is 9 × 30 = 270 ft.

   450 ft − 270 ft = 180 ft, and there are 8 spaces between the letters, so $\frac{180 \text{ ft}}{8} = 22.5$ ft.

4. Possible answer: Map, blueprint

Holt Mathematics

7-7 Percents

Percent means "per one hundred." The decimal grid shows 50%, or 50 out of 100.

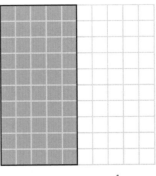

Use the decimal grid to show a model of each percent. Then write the percent as a fraction in simplest form.

1. 25% = ____$\frac{1}{4}$____   **2.** 75% = ____$\frac{3}{4}$____   **3.** 80% = ____$\frac{4}{5}$____

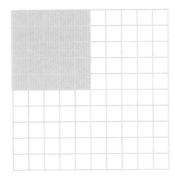   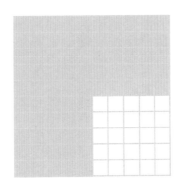   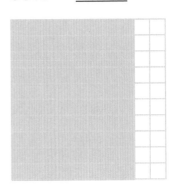

Determine the percent modeled by each decimal grid, and then write it as a fraction in simplest form.

4. 10% = $\frac{1}{10}$ **5.** 30% = $\frac{3}{10}$ **6.** 40% = $\frac{2}{5}$

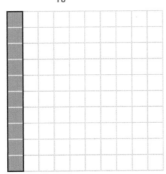   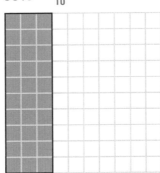   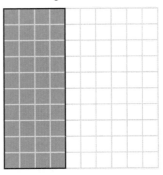

Think and Discuss

7. Explain how to write a percent as a fraction.

Possible answer: Write the percent as the numerator and 100 as the denominator, and then write the fraction in simplest form.

Holt Mathematics

7-8 Percents, Decimals, and Fractions

To report what percent of their fund-raising goal has been reached, a charity uses the number-line model below.

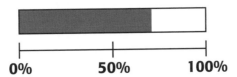

0%   50%   100%

1. Has the charity reached about 50%, about 75%, or about 100% of its goal? about 75%

Complete each number-line model by writing percents above the line and the corresponding fractions below the line.

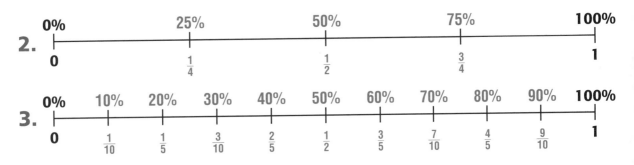

2.

0%	25%	50%	75%	100%
0	$\frac{1}{4}$	$\frac{1}{2}$	$\frac{3}{4}$	1

3.

0%	10%	20%	30%	40%	50%	60%	70%	80%	90%	100%
0	$\frac{1}{10}$	$\frac{1}{5}$	$\frac{3}{10}$	$\frac{2}{5}$	$\frac{1}{2}$	$\frac{3}{5}$	$\frac{7}{10}$	$\frac{4}{5}$	$\frac{9}{10}$	1

Think and Discuss

4. Explain how you matched percents with fractions in numbers **2** and **3.** Possible answer: Write each percent as a fraction in simplest form.

5. Explain how you could label the number lines with decimals. Possible answer: Determine the percent, and then convert the percent to a decimal.

Holt Mathematics

EXPLORATION

7-9 Percent Problems

You can use a number line to find the percent of a number.

```
     0      125      250      375      500
     ├───────┼────────┼────────┼────────┤
    0%                               100%
```

Use the number-line model above to complete each problem.

1. $\frac{125}{500}$ = ___25___ % **2.** $\frac{250}{500}$ = ___50___ % **3.** $\frac{375}{500}$ = ___75___ %

```
     0                                640
     ├───────┼────────┼────────┼────────┤
    0%                               100%
```

Label the number-line model above to find each percent of 640.

4. 50% of 640 is ___320___ .

5. 25% of 640 is ___160___ .

6. 75% of 640 is ___480___ .

Think and Discuss

7. Discuss what it means to find 100% of a number. (*Hint:* What is 100% of 640?) Possible answer: 100% of a number is the number (For example, 100% of 640 is 640.).

8. Explain how you can use number-line models to solve percent problems. Possible answer: Use the whole number line to represent 100% of the given number. Then divide the line into smaller units to find various percents.

Holt Mathematics

7-10 Using Percents

Stores that go out of business often offer big discounts on purchases. In such situations, 50% off sales are common.

Estimate the discount for each item at 50% off. Then calculate the actual discount.

	Item	Price	Estimated Discount	Actual Discount
1.	Shirt	$39.95	$20	$19.98
2.	DVD player	$288.99	$145	$144.50
3.	Speakers	$239.95	$120	$119.98
4.	TV	$1,035.29	$500	$517.65
5.	MP3 player	$247.99	$125	$124.00

Think and Discuss

6. **Discuss** the estimation strategies you used.
7. **Explain** whether a one-time 50% discount is equivalent to two consecutive 25% discounts. (*Hint:* Use $100.00 as the base amount.)

6. Possible answer: Round each price to the nearest multiple of 10 and then divide by 2.

7. Possible answer: No, a 50% discount on $100 is $50. A 25% discount reduces the price to $75, and another 25% discount reduces the price by another $18.75 for a total discount of $25 + $18.85 = $43.75. The two discounts are not equivalent.

8-1 Building Blocks of Geometry

Geometry can be used to describe the physical world around us. Check the box of the geometry term that each real-world item represents.

		Point	Line Segment	Plane
1.	A freckle	✓		
2.	A strand of hair		✓	
3.	A poster			✓
4.	A pixel on your calculator screen	✓		
5.	A period at the end of a sentence	✓		
6.	A guitar string		✓	
7.	The minute hand of a clock		✓	
8.	A computer screen			✓

Think and Discuss

9. **Describe** the characteristics of the items that you classified as *points* in the table above. Possible answer: The items are very small and have no length.

10. **Describe** the characteristics of the items that you classified as *line segments* in the table above. Possible answer: The items are long and thin, and they start and end at specific points.

Holt Mathematics

8-2 Measuring and Classifying Angles

An angle is formed by two rays that have a common endpoint. Right angles measure 90° and are shaped like a letter L. You can estimate an angle measure by comparing the angle with a right angle.

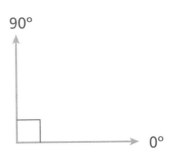

Estimate the measure of each angle. Then measure the angle with a protractor. Estimates may vary.

		Estimate	Actual
1.		45°	45°
2.		125°	125°
3.		20°	20°
4.		95°	95°

Think and Discuss

5. Discuss how you estimated the angle measures. Possible answer: Determine how much larger or smaller the angle is than a 90° angle.

Holt Mathematics

8-3 Angle Relationships

The line segments in some letters, symbols, and numbers form angles.

Numbers 1–5 describe types of angle pairs. Determine which marked angle pairs in the figures apply to each description, and then check the appropriate boxes.

		Z	X	F	↗	4
1.	Congruent angles: same measure	✓	✓	✓	✓	✓
2.	Vertical angles: opposite each other when two lines intersect		✓			
3.	Adjacent angles: side by side with a common vertex and ray			✓	✓	✓
4.	Complementary angles: sum equals 90°				✓	
5.	Supplementary angles: sum equals 180°			✓		✓

Think and Discuss

6. Discuss other examples of vertical angles in the real world.

Possible answer: the angles formed by the legs of a picnic table

Holt Mathematics

8-4 Classifying Lines

The table shows pairs of intersecting lines, pairs of parallel lines, and pairs of perpendicular lines.

Intersecting Lines	Parallel Lines	Perpendicular Lines

1. Draw your own examples of intersecting lines, parallel lines, and perpendicular lines.

Think and Discuss

2. **Describe** how you can tell if two lines are parallel.

3. **Discuss** what makes perpendicular lines different from other lines that intersect.

Possible answers:

1.

2. The two lines do not intersect.
3. Perpendicular lines intersect at a right angle.

67

Holt Mathematics

8-5 Triangles

You can classify triangles by the measures of their angles.

Measure the angles of each triangle. Then check the box that gives the correct classification of the triangle.

	Acute Triangle: has only acute (less than 90°) angles	Obtuse Triangle: has one obtuse (greater than 90°) angle	Right Triangle: has one right (90°) angle
1.			✓
2.	✓		
3.		✓	

Think and Discuss

4. **Find** the sum of the angle measures in each triangle. 180°
5. **Make** a generalization about the sum of the angle measures in a triangle. The sum of the angle measures in any triangle is 180°.

Holt Mathematics

8-6 Quadrilaterals

Find a real-world example for each quadrilateral. Possible answers:

	Quadrilateral	Example
1.	Parallelogram	a piece of a tangram puzzle
2.	Rhombus	the diamond shape in a deck of cards
3.	Rectangle	a window
4.	Trapezoid	the side view of a yogurt container

Think and Discuss

5. **Discuss** how all the quadrilaterals are similar. Possible answer: All have four sides.

6. **Explain** what is special about the rectangle.
   Possible answer: The rectangle has four right angles.

Holt Mathematics

8-7 Polygons

In a *regular polygon,* all sides are congruent and all angles are congruent.

Name each polygon and determine whether it is regular. Use number 1 as an example.

	Polygon	Name	Regular?
1.		Triangle	no
2.		Triangle	yes
3.		Quadrilateral	yes
4.		Quadrilateral	no
5.		Pentagon	no
6.		Pentagon	yes

Think and Discuss

7. Explain how you classified each polygon in numbers 2–6.

Possible answer: Count the number of sides to name the polygon. Then check to see if all sides are congruent and all angles are congruent.

Holt Mathematics

EXPLORATION

8-8 Geometric Patterns

Look for a pattern, and draw the next three figures in the sequence.

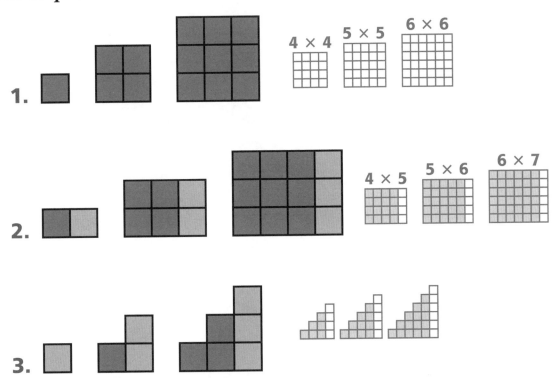

Think and Discuss

4. **Explain** how the sequence in number **2** is built on the sequence in number **1.** Possible answer: The sequence in number 2 is the same as that in number 1 but with an additional column.

5. **Describe** in words the sequence in number **3.**

Possible answer: Each time a new column is added, it has one more square than the previous column.

Holt Mathematics

8-9 Congruence

Congruent figures are exactly the same shape and size.

1. Connect two congruent figures with a line. Two congruent rectangles have been connected for you to use as a guide.

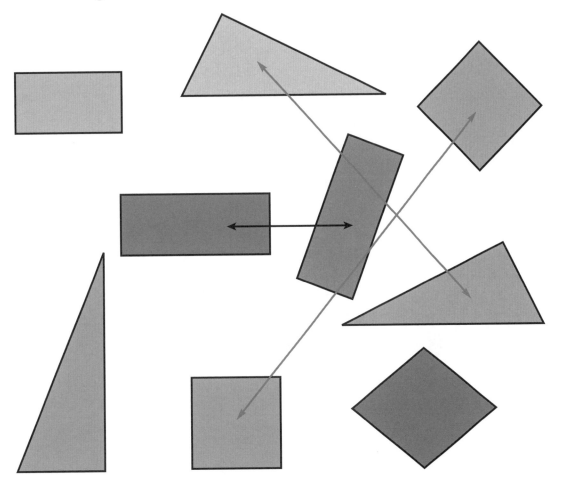

2. Measure the sides and angles of each pair of connected figures to be sure that they are congruent.

Think and Discuss

3. **Give examples** of congruent figures that occur in the real world. Possible answer: figures made with the same rubber stamp; postage stamps taken from the same sheet

Holt Mathematics

8-10 Transformations

The green triangle is a *reflection* of the blue triangle across the solid vertical line.

1. Reflect the green triangle across the horizontal line, and then reflect the resulting triangle across the vertical line.

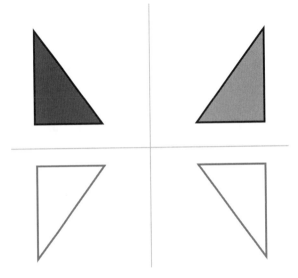

The orange triangle is a *translation* of the yellow triangle down and to the right.

2. Translate the orange triangle up and to the right.

Think and Discuss

3. **Define** *reflection* in your own words. Possible answer: A reflection flips a figure.
4. **Define** *translation* in your own words. Possible answer: A translation slides a figure.

73

Holt Mathematics

8-11 Line Symmetry

A figure has *line symmetry* if you can draw a line through it to form two congruent shapes that are reflections of each other.

Draw as many lines of symmetry through each figure as possible. Then give the total number of lines drawn in each.

		How Many Lines of Symmetry?	
1.	■	⊠	4
2.	▲	△	3
3.	⬡	✳	6
4.	▲	△	1

Think and Discuss

5. Discuss the characteristics of the figures that have more than one line of symmetry. Possible answer: They are regular polygons.

6. Discuss the characteristics of the figures that have only one line of symmetry. Possible answer: The sides of the figure are not all congruent.

Holt Mathematics

9-1 Understanding Customary Units of Measure

Different units of measure are used for measuring length, weight, and capacity. Capacity is the amount that a container can hold.

1. Decide whether each of the units of measure below is used to measure length, weight, or capacity. Write the name of the unit in the appropriate column of the table.

Pint   Pound   Inch   Ton

Foot   Quart   Mile   Gallon

Yard   Ounce   Cup   Fluid Ounce

Length	Weight	Capacity
Inch	Ounce	Fluid Ounce
Foot	Pound	Cup
Yard	Ton	Pint
Mile		Quart
		Gallon

Think and Discuss

2. **Describe** an object that could be measured using yards.
Possible answer: fabric, ribbon, carpet
3. **Explain** how you would decide whether to measure an object using inches or feet. Possible answer: Use inches for shorter objects and feet for longer objects.

Holt Mathematics

9-2 Understanding Metric Units of Measure

In the metric system, the basic unit of length is the meter. One meter (1 m) is about the width of a classroom doorway. Other metric units of length are based on the meter.

Unit	Fraction of a Meter	Decimal Part of a Meter
Millimeter	$\frac{1}{1,000}$ of a meter	0.001 m
Centimeter	$\frac{1}{100}$ of a meter	0.01 m
Decimeter	$\frac{1}{10}$ of a meter	0.1 m

1. Which of the units listed is the smallest? How do you know?
milliliter; $\frac{1}{1,000} < \frac{1}{100} < \frac{1}{10}$

2. Which of the units listed is the largest? How do you know?
decimeter; $\frac{1}{1,000} > \frac{1}{100} > \frac{1}{10}$

3. In the metric system, the basic unit of capacity is the liter (L). The prefixes *milli-*, *centi-*, and *deci-* are used in the same way to create other units of capacity. Complete the table.

Unit	Fraction of a Liter	Decimal Part of a Liter
Milliliter	$\frac{1}{1,000}$? of a liter	0.001 L ?
Centiliter	$\frac{1}{100}$? of a liter	0.01 L ?
Deciliter	$\frac{1}{10}$? of a liter	0.1 L ?

Think and Discuss

4. **Explain** which is longer, a stick that is 5 centimeters long or a stick that is 5 decimeters long. The 5 decimeter stick is longer because 1 decimeter is longer than 1 centimeter.

5. **Explain** which holds more, a container with a capacity of 7 milliliters or a container with a capacity of 7 centiliters.

The container with a capacity of 7 centiliters holds more because 1 centiliter is more than 1 milliliter.

Holt Mathematics

9-3 Converting Customary Units

One foot is equal to 12 inches. You can use this fact to explore the relationship between feet and inches.

1. Complete the table.

Feet	1	2	3	4	5	6	7	8
Inches	12	24	36	48	60	72	84	96

2. Complete the table.

Feet	9	10	11	12	13	14	15	16
Inches	108	120	132	144	156	168	180	192

3. If you are given a length in feet, how can you convert the length to inches?   Multiply by 12.

4. If you are given a length in inches, how can you convert the length to feet?   Divide by 12.

Think and Discuss

5. Describe what you would do to convert 324 inches to feet.

6. Explain how you could use the above tables to convert 3.5 feet to inches.

5.   Divide by 12. 324 ÷ 12 = 27, so 324 in. equals 27 ft.

6.   Possible answer: 3.5 ft is halfway between two values in the row for feet, so the equivalent length in inches is halfway between the corresponding values, 36 in. and 48 in. Therefore, 3.5 ft = 42 in.

Holt Mathematics

9-4 Converting Metric Units

Because the metric table is based on powers of 10, it is important to be able to multiply and divide quickly by powers of 10.

1. Complete the table by multiplying by 10, by 100, and by 1,000. You may use a calculator or any other method you wish. Look for patterns as you work.

Number	× 10	× 100	× 1,000
42	420	4,200	42,000
3.8	38	380	3,800
0.97	9.7	97	970
0.065	0.65	6.5	65

2. Complete the table by dividing by 10, by 100, and by 1,000. You may use a calculator or any other method you wish. Look for patterns as you work.

Number	÷ 10	÷ 100	÷ 1,000
512	51.2	5.12	0.512
63.9	6.39	0.639	0.0639
4.05	0.405	0.0405	0.00405
0.772	0.0772	0.00772	0.000772

Think and Discuss

3. **Describe** shortcuts for multiplying by 10, by 100, and by 1,000.

4. **Explain** shortcuts for dividing by 10, by 100, and by 1,000.

3. Possible answer: To multiply by 10, move the decimal point one place to the right. To multiply by 100, move the decimal point two places to the right. To multiply by 1,000, move the decimal point three places to the right.

4. Possible answer: To divide by 10, move the decimal point one place to the left. To divide by 100, move the decimal point two places to the left. To divide by 1,000, move the decimal point three places to the left.

Holt Mathematics

9-5 Time and Temperature

One hour is divided into 60 minutes. You can use proportional thinking to explore the relationship between hours and minutes.

1. How many minutes are there in 2 hours? in 3 hours? 120; 180

2. How many minutes are there in $\frac{1}{2}$ hour? in $\frac{1}{4}$ hour? 30; 15

3. Complete the table.

Hours	$\frac{1}{10}$	$\frac{1}{5}$	4	6	8	10
Minutes	6	12	240	360	480	600

4. What fraction of an hour is 2 minutes? $\frac{1}{30}$

5. In general, how can you convert any number of minutes to hours? Divide by 60.

6. In general, how can you convert any number of hours to minutes? Multiply by 60.

Think and Discuss

7. Explain how to write 23 minutes as a fraction of an hour.

8. Discuss how you could write 72 minutes in terms of hours and minutes.

7. Divide by 60. The fraction is $\frac{23}{60}$.

8. Possible answer: Subtract 60 minutes, which is 1 hour, and there are 12 minutes left. So the equivalent time is 1 hour, 12 minutes.

Holt Mathematics

9-6 Finding Angle Measures in Polygons

The figures show the measures of several angles.

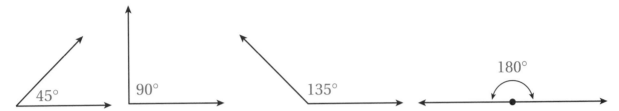

You can use these angles as benchmarks to help you estimate the measures of other angles.

Estimate the measure of each angle.

1. Possible answer: 20°

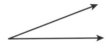

2. Possible answer: 60°

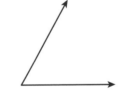

3. Possible answer: 100°

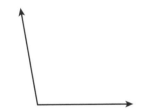

4. Possible answer: 170°

Think and Discuss

5. Explain how you could use the corner of an index card to help you estimate angle measures. Possible answer: Use the corner of the card as a benchmark for 90° angles. You can also fold the corner in half so that the edges meet to create a benchmark for 45° angles.

6. Describe how you could use the corner of an index card to draw a 135° angle. (*Hint:* Consider folding the corner of the card.) Possible answer: Use the corner of the card to draw a 90° angle. Then fold the corner in half so that edges meet to create a 45° angle, and trace this angle next to the 90° angle.

Holt Mathematics

9-7 Perimeter

Felicia is working with her dad to design a deck for their yard. They sketch the floor space on grid paper with the side length of each square representing 2 feet.

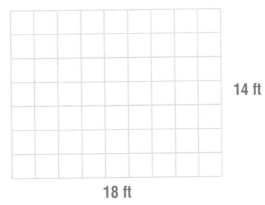

14 ft

18 ft

1. Label the dimensions in feet of the deck.

2. The final task in building the deck is to nail a trim piece all the way around the deck. Find the distance around the deck. **64 ft**

3. The distance around the deck is called the *perimeter.* What are three other real-world situations in which you might want to find the perimeter? **Possible answer: fencing, putting a baseboard around a room, framing a picture**

Think and Discuss

4. **Discuss** your method for finding the perimeter of the deck.

5. **Explain** how you could write a formula for perimeter of a rectangle using ℓ for length and w for width.

4. Possible answer: Add the lengths of the sides.

5. $P = 2\ell + 2w$

Holt Mathematics

9-8 Circles and Circumference

People in ancient civilizations learned to estimate the distance around a circle (*circumference*) by multiplying the distance across (*diameter*) by three.

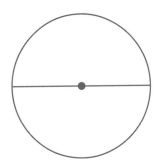

1. Does the distance around the circle above look like three times the diameter? Yes

2. The table below contains actual measurements, to the nearest tenth of a centimeter, of two cans. Use a calculator to find the ratio $\frac{\text{circumference}}{\text{diameter}}$.

Object	Diameter (cm)	Circumference (cm)	Circumference Diameter
Juice can	5.2	16.3	3.13
Coffee can	15.7	49.3	3.14

3. Are the $\frac{\text{circumference}}{\text{diameter}}$ ratios you found in number 2 reasonably close to 3? Yes

Think and Discuss

4. Discuss whether the ratio $\frac{\text{circumference}}{\text{diameter}}$ changes according to the size of the circle. No, the ratio is always close to 3.

Holt Mathematics

10-1 Estimating and Finding Area

Mr. and Mrs. Domínguez want to have the bottom of their pool refinished. A sketch of the pool is shown below with the side length of each square representing 1 yard. Before they begin the refinishing project, they have to estimate the area in square yards of the bottom of the pool.

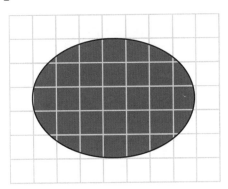

1. Estimate the area, in square yards, of the bottom of the pool. **25 yds**

2. Compare your estimate with the estimates of others in your class, and then average your estimates. **Answers will vary.**

3. What are three other real-world situations in which you might want to estimate area? **Possible answers: painting a wall, installing floor tiles, planting a garden**

Think and Discuss

4. **Discuss** the strategies you used for estimating the area of the bottom of the pool. **Possible answer: count whole squares and then account for partial squares.**

5. **Explain** how you could use squares to help you estimate the areas of irregular shapes. **Possible answer: Put a grid over the irregular shapes and count whole and partial squares.**

Holt Mathematics

10-2 Area of Triangles and Trapezoids

You can use what you know about the area of a parallelogram to develop a formula for the area of a triangle.

1. Fold a sheet of paper in half. Use a ruler to draw a triangle on one side of the folded sheet. Label the base and height of the triangle as shown.

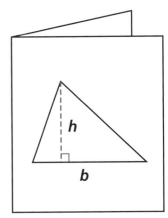

2. Cut out the triangle, cutting through both layers of the folded paper. This will create two congruent triangles.

3. Arrange the two triangles to form a parallelogram.

4. What is the height of the parallelogram? What is its base? *h; b*

5. What is the area of the parallelogram? *bh*

6. How is the area of the triangle related to the area of the parallelogram? The area of the triangle is half that of the parallelogram.

Think and Discuss

7. **Show** how to write a formula for the area of a triangle with base b and height h. $A = \frac{1}{2}bh$

8. **Explain** how to use your formula to find the area of this triangle. Substitute $b = 10$ and $h = 8$ in the formula. $A = 40$ cm^2

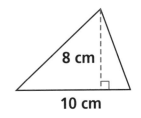

8 cm

10 cm

Holt Mathematics

10-3 Area of Composite Figures

Phil and Louise are planning to sod their backyard. Sod is sold in square yards. They sketched their yard on a piece of graph paper, where the side length of each square represents 1 yard.

Possible answer for 1a.

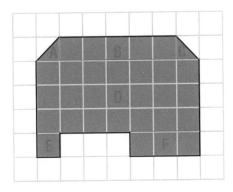

1. **a.** Divide the figure into several simpler figures.

   b. Name each figure from part **a.** Possible answers: A and C are triangles; B, D, and F are rectangles; E is a square.

   c. Find the area in square yards of each figure.
   A: $\frac{1}{2}$; B: 5; C: $\frac{1}{2}$; D: 21; E: 1; F: 3

   d. Add the areas in part **c.** 31 yd²

Think and Discuss

2. **Discuss** the strategies you used for finding area.

3. **Explain** how you could use squares to help you find the areas of irregular shapes.

2. Possible answer: Divide a complex figure into simpler figures for which you can find the area.

3. Possible answer: Place a grid of squares on the irregular shape and count the squares.

Holt Mathematics

10-4 Comparing Perimeter and Area

Suzanne is enlarging a color copy of a 3 in. by 5 in. photograph to 6 in. by 10 in. A model is shown below.

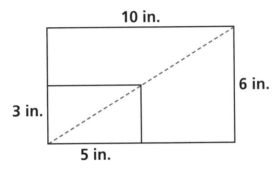

Find the perimeter of each color copy.

	Color Copy	Perimeter = 2 · Length + 2 · Width
1.	3 in. by 5 in.	$2 \cdot 5 + 2 \cdot 3 = 10 + 6 = 16$ in.
2.	6 in. by 10 in.	$2 \cdot 10 + 2 \cdot 6 = 20 + 12 = 32$ in.

3. How do the perimeters compare? The perimeter of the larger copy is twice that of the smaller one.

Find the area of each color copy.

	Color Copy	Area = Length · Width
4.	3 in. by 5 in.	$3 \cdot 5 = 15$ in^2
5.	6 in. by 10 in.	$6 \cdot 10 = 60$ in^2

6. How do the areas compare? The area of the larger copy is 4 times that of the smaller one.

Think and Discuss

7. Explain how you compared the perimeters. Possible answer: Write a ratio of large to small: $\frac{32}{16} = \frac{2}{1}$

8. Explain how you compared the areas. Possible answer: Write a ratio of large to small: $\frac{60}{15} = \frac{4}{1}$

Holt Mathematics

EXPLORATION

10-5 Area of Circles

You can use estimation to help you investigate the area of circles.

1. Estimate the area of the circle by counting whole and partial squares.
   Possible answer: 50

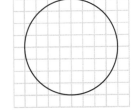

2. What is the radius r of the circle? 4

3. Calculate πr^2 using 3.14 for pi. 50.24

4. How does the value of πr^2 compare to your estimate of the circle's area? The value of πr^2 is very close to the estimated area.

5. Repeat the process for this circle. First estimate the area by counting whole and partial squares. Possible answer: 78

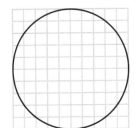

6. What is the radius of the circle? 5

7. Calculate πr^2 using 3.14 for pi. 78.5

8. How does the value of πr^2 compare to your estimate of the circle's area? The value of πr^2 is very close to the estimated area.

Think and Discuss

9. **Describe** any shortcuts you found for counting the squares.

10. **Explain** how you can use what you discovered to write a formula for the area of a circle with radius r. $A = \pi r^2$

9. Possible answer: Count the number of whole and partial squares in one quarter of the circle and multiply by 4.

Holt Mathematics

10-6 Three-Dimensional Figures

A cube is a solid figure with six faces, twelve edges, and eight vertices.

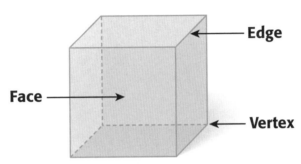

Determine how many faces, edges, and vertices each solid figure has.

		Faces	Edges	Vertices
1.		5	9	6
2.		5	8	5
3.		7	15	10

Think and Discuss

4. Explain how many edges it takes to form a vertex. at least 3

5. Explain how many faces it takes to form an edge. exactly 2

Holt Mathematics

10-7 Volume of Prisms

Volume is the number of cubic units that fill a space. Notice how the volume of a rectangular prism increases as the height increases.

$V = 6$ cubic units

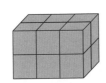

$V = 12$ cubic units

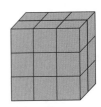

$V = 18$ cubic units

Find the volume of each rectangular prism

1.

8 cubic units

2.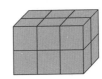

12 cubic units

3.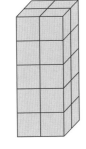

20 cubic units

4.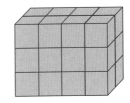

24 cubic units

Think and Discuss

5. **Explain** how you found the volume of each rectangular prism. Possible answer: Count the number of cubes.

6. **Discuss** why the formulas $V = $ base $\cdot$ height and $V = $ length $\cdot$ width $\cdot$ height are equivalent. Possible answer: The area of the base is length $\cdot$ width, so you can replace "base" in the first formula with length $\cdot$ width.

Holt Mathematics

10-8 Volume of Cylinders

The area of the base of a soup can is 4.9 in², and the height is 4 in. To find the volume of this can, multiply the area of the base times the height.

volume = area of base · height ($V = Bh$)

$V = 4.9 \cdot 4 = 19.6$ in³

The soup can has a volume of 19.6 in³.

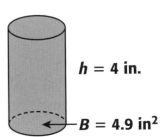

$h = 4$ in.

$B = 4.9$ in²

Find the volume of each cylinder.

	Area of Base	Height	Volume = Area of Base · Height
1.	12.6 in²	8 in.	100.8 in³
2.	28.3 cm²	10 cm	283 cm³
3.	3.14 ft²	2 ft	6.28 ft³
4.	113.1 in²	12 in.	1,357.2 in³
5.	176.7 cm²	25 cm	4,417.5 cm³

Think and Discuss

6. Explain how to find the volume of a cylinder. Multiply the area of the base times the height.

7. Discuss why the formulas $V = B \cdot h$ and $V = \pi \cdot r^2 \cdot h$ are equivalent (r = radius). Possible answer: *B* is the area of the base, and the area of a circle is πr^2, so the *B* in the first formula can be replaced by πr^2.

Holt Mathematics

10-9 Surface Area

You can use grid paper to make nets that cover boxes, or rectangular solids. The area of the net is the *surface area of the solid.*

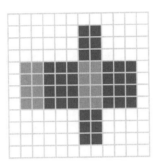

1. Find the combined area of the blue rectangles (the sides of the box). **36 square units**

2. Find the combined area of the green rectangles (the top and bottom of the box). **16 square units**

3. Add the areas you found in numbers **1** and **2.** This is the surface area of the box. **52 square units**

4. On the grid below, draw a different net that can cover a box, and find its surface area. **Possible answer shown below; 38 square units**

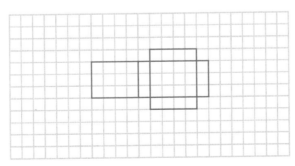

Think and Discuss

5. Explain how you can use a net to find surface area. **Possible answer: Use the net to find the area of each face of the solid. Then add the areas.**

Holt Mathematics

11-1 Integers in Real-World Situations

Integers can be represented with two-color counters. A red counter represents −1, and a yellow counter represents 1. Each red and yellow pair is called a zero pair.

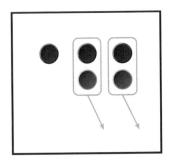

Zero pair

A zero pair has a value of zero. To find the value on an integer mat, remove zero pairs.

The value on this mat is −1.

Possible answer:

Find the value on each mat.

1. −2

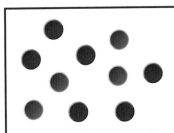

2. 2

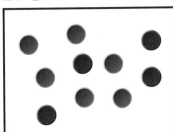

3. −2

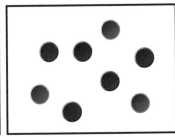

4. Create four different mats that show a value of −1.

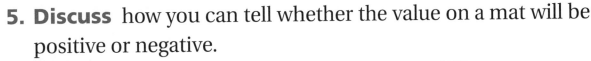

Think and Discuss

5. Discuss how you can tell whether the value on a mat will be positive or negative.

6. Describe the strategies you used to create different mats that show a value of −1.

5. Possible answer: If there are more positive counters, the mat's value is positive; if there are more negative counters, the value is negative.

6. Possible answer: there should be one more negative counter than positive on the mat.

Holt Mathematics

11-2 Comparing and Ordering Integers

1. The completed table shows the average January temperatures in degrees Fahrenheit and degrees Celsius for some U.S. cities. Complete the other table by ordering the cities from warmest to coolest.

	°F	°C
Juneau, AK	24	−4
Phoenix, AZ	54	12
Atlanta, GA	41	5
Des Moines, IA	19	−7
Bismarck, ND	9	−13
Houston, TX	50	10
Boston, MA	29	−2
Kansas City, MO	26	−3

Source: Statistical Abstract of the United States

Warmest

	°F	°C
Phoenix, AZ	54	12
Houston, TX	50	10
Atlanta, GA	41	5
Boston, MA	29	−2
Kansas City, MO	26	−3
Juneau, AK	24	−4
Des Moines, IA	19	−7
Bismarck, ND	9	−13

Coolest

Boston is colder than Houston because **29 < 50** in degrees Fahrenheit and **−2 < 10** in degrees Celsius.

Houston is warmer than Boston because **50 > 29** in degrees Fahrenheit and **10 > −2** in degrees Celsius.

2. Use inequality symbols to compare the Kansas City temperature in degrees Celsius with each of the other temperatures in degrees Celsius. −3 < 12; −3 < 10; −3 < 5; −3 < −2; −3 > −4; −3 > −7; −3 > −13

Think and Discuss

3. **Describe** your method for ordering the cities from warmest to coolest. Possible answer: Order the Fahrenheit temperatures from greatest to least, and then write the corresponding Celsius temperatures in the appropriate column.

93

Holt Mathematics

EXPLORATION

11-3 The Coordinate Plane

On the *coordinate plane* below, the color of the first number in each ordered pair matches the color of the *x-axis,* and the color of the second number in each ordered pair matches the color of the *y-axis.*

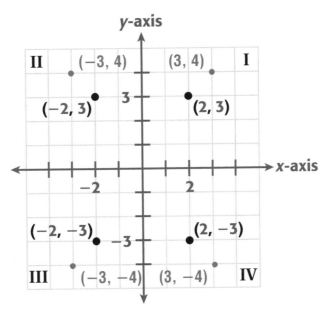

1. The four points graphed are labeled with their ordered pairs. How are these four ordered pairs alike? How are they different? Possible answer: All of the ordered pairs include 2 or −2 and 3 or −3. The ordered pairs describe points in different parts of the coordinate plane.

2. Plot the points (3, 4), (−3, 4), (−3, −4), and (3, −4) on the same coordinate plane.

Think and Discuss

3. **Describe** what each number in an ordered pair tells you.

Possible answer: The first tells how many units to move left or right; the second tells how many units to move up or down.

Holt Mathematics

11-4 Adding Integers

You can use a thermometer to model addition of integers.

1. Suppose the temperature starts at −10°F and increases 30° during the day. Complete the addition statement to show the new temperature.

   −10° + 30° = ___20°___

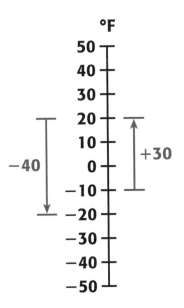

2. Suppose the temperature starts at 20°F and drops 40° overnight. Complete the addition statement to show the new temperature.

   20° + (−40°) = ___−20°___

3. Draw a thermometer and show 20° + (−10°). Find the sum. **10°**

Think and Discuss

4. **Describe** how to add a positive integer using a thermometer.
5. **Describe** how to add a negative integer using a thermometer.

4. Possible answer: To add a positive integer on the thermometer, count upward on the thermometer.

5. Possible answer: To add a negative integer on the thermometer, count downward on the thermometer.

Holt Mathematics

EXPLORATION

11-5 Subtracting Integers

You can use a number line to model subtracting integers.

To subtract 20 from 50, begin at the number being subtracted, 20, and count the number of units to the number 50.

The direction is **right**, so the difference is **positive**.

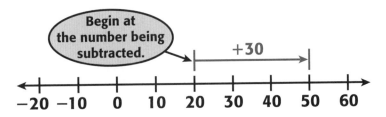

$50 - 20 = 30$

To subtract -20 from -60, begin at the number being subtracted, -20, and count the number of units to the number -60.

The direction is **left**, so the difference is **negative**.

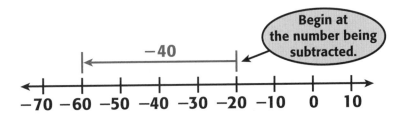

$-60 - (-20) = -40$

Use a number line to find each difference.

1. $12 - 10 =$ __2__

2. $15 - 20 =$ __-5__

3. $-8 - 5 =$ __-13__

4. $-6 - (-4) =$ __-2__

5. $2 - (-4) =$ __6__

6. $7 - (-2) =$ __9__

Think and Discuss

7. Describe how to use a number line to model subtraction.

Possible answer: Begin at the number being subtracted, and count the number of units to the first number in the subtraction expression. If you moved right, the difference is positive; if you moved left, the difference is negative.

Holt Mathematics

11-6 Multiplying Integers

Complete each table.

1.

$2 \cdot 3 = 6$	$-2 \cdot (3) = -6$	$2 \cdot (-3) = -6$	$-2 \cdot (-3) = 6$
$2 \cdot 2 = 4$	$-2 \cdot (2) = -4$	$2 \cdot (-2) = -4$	$-2 \cdot (-2) = 4$
$2 \cdot 1 = 2$	$-2 \cdot (1) = -2$	$2 \cdot (-1) = -2$	$-2 \cdot (-1) = 2$

2.

$3 \cdot 3 = 9$	$-3 \cdot (3) = -9$	$3 \cdot (-3) = -9$	$-3 \cdot (-3) = 9$
$3 \cdot 2 = 6$	$-3 \cdot (2) = -6$	$3 \cdot (-2) = -6$	$-3 \cdot (-2) = 6$
$3 \cdot 1 = 3$	$-3 \cdot (1) = -3$	$3 \cdot (-1) = -3$	$-3 \cdot (-1) = 3$

3.

$4 \cdot 3 = 12$	$-4 \cdot (3) = -12$	$4 \cdot (-3) = -12$	$-4 \cdot (-3) = 12$
$4 \cdot 2 = 8$	$-4 \cdot (2) = -8$	$4 \cdot (-2) = -8$	$-4 \cdot (-2) = 8$
$4 \cdot 1 = 4$	$-4 \cdot (1) = -4$	$4 \cdot (-1) = -4$	$-4 \cdot (-1) = 4$

Think and Discuss

4. Describe the patterns you notice in each of the tables.

Possible answer: When two factors have the same sign, the product is positive. When two factors have opposite signs, the product is negative.

Holt Mathematics

11-7 Dividing Integers

For each multiplication statement, you can write two related division statements.

Multiplication statement	Division statements
$2 \cdot 3 = 6$	$6 \div 3 = 2$ and $6 \div 2 = 3$

Complete each table.

1.

Multiply	$4 \cdot (-3) = -12$	$-4 \cdot (-3) = 12$	$-4 \cdot 3 = -12$
Divide	$-12 \div 4 = -3$	$12 \div (-4) = -3$	$-12 \div (-4) = 3$
	$-12 \div (-3) = 4$	$12 \div (-3) = -4$	$-12 \div 3 = -4$

2.

Multiply	$2 \cdot (-5) = -10$	$-2 \cdot (-5) = 10$	$-2 \cdot 5 = -10$
Divide	$-10 \div 2 = -5$	$10 \div (-2) = -5$	$-10 \div (-2) = 5$
	$-10 \div (-5) = 2$	$10 \div (-5) = -2$	$-10 \div 5 = -2$

3.

Multiply	$8 \cdot (-3) = -24$	$-8 \cdot (-3) = 24$	$-8 \cdot 3 = -24$
Divide	$-24 \div 8 = -3$	$24 \div (-8) = -3$	$-24 \div (-8) = 3$
	$-24 \div (-3) = 8$	$24 \div (-3) = -8$	$-24 \div 3 = -8$

Think and Discuss

4. Describe what you think the sign rules are for dividing a positive integer by a negative integer, a negative integer by a positive integer, and a negative integer by a negative integer.

Possible answer: Dividing a positive integer by a negative integer and dividing a negative integer by a positive integer both result in a negative quotient. Dividing a negative integer by a negative integer results in a positive quotient.

Holt Mathematics

EXPLORATION

11-8 Solving Integer Equations

You can use algebra tiles to model solving integer equations.

− represents −1.
+ represents 1.

+ represents an unknown amount x.

The equation $x - 3 = 5$ is modeled.

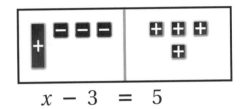

$$x - 3 = 5$$

To get x alone on one side, add three positive tiles to each side of the mat. This allows you to remove three zero pairs from the left side.

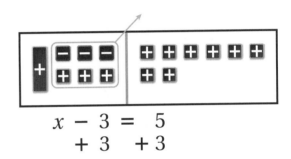

$$x - 3 = 5$$
$$+ 3 \quad + 3$$

The solution is 8.

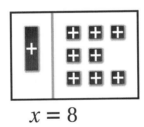

$$x = 8$$

Use algebra tiles to solve each equation.

1. $x + 5 = 9$ $x = 4$ **2.** $x - 6 = 2$ $x = 8$ **3.** $x + 4 = -1$ $x = -5$

4. $6 = x - 7$ $x = 13$ **5.** $8 = x + 2$ $x = 6$ **6.** $3 = x - 9$ $x = 12$

Think and Discuss

7. Explain how you know whether to add positive tiles or negative tiles to each side of the mat. Possible answer: Add positive tiles when a value from x. Add negative tiles when a value is added to x.

Holt Mathematics

11-9 Tables and Functions

A school has scheduled a trip for 210 students to a theme park. The school can rent up to six buses for $200 each. Each bus seats a maximum of 60 students. Tickets to the theme park cost $25 per student.

1. Use the first example as a guide to complete the table.

Group Number	Number of Students	Cost of Bus Rental and Tickets	Total Cost
1	10	$200 + 25 \cdot 10 = 200 + 250$	$450.00
2	20	$200 + 25 \cdot 20 = 200 + 500$	$700
3	30	$200 + 25 \cdot 30 = 200 + 750$	$950
4	40	$200 + 25 \cdot 40 = 200 + 1{,}000$	$1,200
5	50	$200 + 25 \cdot 50 = 200 + 1{,}250$	$1,450
6	60	$200 + 25 \cdot 60 = 200 + 1{,}500$	$1,700

2. What numbers in the table remain constant? $200 and $25

3. What numbers in the table vary? number of students; total cost

4. Use the cost of the bus ($200), the cost of each ticket ($25), and the number of students (x) to write an equation for the total cost (c). (*Hint:* Look at the middle column of the table to write the equation.) $c = 200 + 25x$

Think and Discuss

5. Explain what makes the total cost of a group vary. the number of students

6. Discuss possible ways of reducing the total cost of taking 210 students to the theme park. Possible answer: Put more students on each bus so that fewer buses are needed.

Holt Mathematics

EXPLORATION

11-10 Graphing Functions

To graph a *linear equation,* you can plot ordered pairs from a table of x- and y-values as points on a coordinate grid.

The table and graph at right model the function $y = x + 2$.

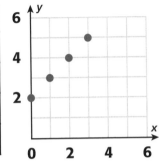

x	y
0	2
1	3
2	4
3	5

Graph each set of ordered pairs on the coordinate grid.

1. $y = x - 2$

x	y
2	0
3	1
4	2
5	3

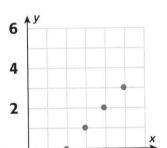

2. $y = x + 1$

x	y
1	2
2	3
3	4
4	5

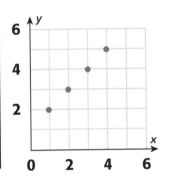

Use the points on each graph to complete each table.

3.

x	y
1	1
2	2
3	3
4	4

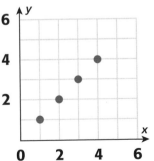

4.

x	y
0	2
2	3
4	4
6	5

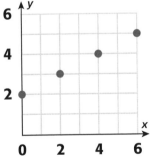

Think and Discuss

5. Explain how to use the points on the graph of a linear equation to write a table of ordered pairs. Possible answer: For each point, determine the x- and y-coordinates and write the values in the table.

101

Holt Mathematics

12-1 Introduction to Probability

Probability describes how likely it is that an event will occur. For example, it is likely that a dog will eat a treat, and it is unlikely that a human being will live 200 years.

Tell whether each event is likely or unlikely to happen.

	Event	Probability
1.	Having a blackout during a thunderstorm	likely
2.	Losing your money in an old vending machine	likely
3.	Winning the lottery	unlikely
4.	Finding a $100 bill on the street	unlikely
5.	Passing a test for which you studied very hard	likely
6.	Being in a traffic jam at 5:00 P.M. on Monday	likely
7.	Hearing your favorite song when you first turn on the radio	unlikely

Think and Discuss

8. Describe an event that is impossible. Possible answer: A month has 32 days.

9. Describe an event that is certain to happen.

Possible answer: Tuesday will be the day after Monday.

Holt Mathematics

12-2 Experimental Probability

You can find the *experimental probability* of an event by dividing the number of times an event occurs by the total number of times the experiment is performed.

$$\text{probability} = \frac{\text{number of times an event occurs}}{\text{total number of trials}}$$

1. The data in the table show the number of free throws five players made in a season. Find the $\frac{\text{made}}{\text{attempts}}$ ratio for each player.

	Bo	Jack	Ali	Kim	José
Free Throws Made	30	32	15	36	24
Attempts	48	64	25	48	49
$\frac{\text{Made}}{\text{Attempts}}$	$\frac{5}{8}$	$\frac{1}{2}$	$\frac{3}{5}$	$\frac{3}{4}$	$\frac{24}{49}$

2. Which player has the best chance of making a free throw?

Kim

3. Which player has the worst chance of making a free throw?

José

Think and Discuss

4. **Discuss** how you determined the answers for numbers 2 and 3. Possible answer: Determine who had the greatest/least ratio.

5. **Explain** how to write each $\frac{\text{made}}{\text{attempts}}$ ratio as a percent.

Write the fraction as a decimal and then multiply by 100.

Holt Mathematics

12-3 Counting Methods and Sample Spaces

A teacher made a quiz with three true or false questions. You can make an organized list to determine all of the answer possibilities for the three questions.

1. Complete the tree diagram to list all possible answer outcomes.

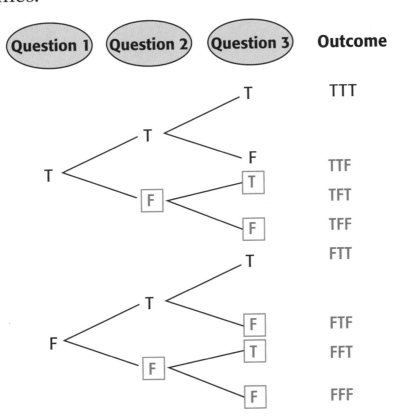

2. How many outcomes are possible? 8

Think and Discuss

3. Discuss your method for organizing the list of outcomes.

4. Explain how you could determine the number of outcomes possible with four questions.

3. Possible answer: Read the outcomes on each branch.

4. Possible answer: Add another set of branches at the end of each branch of the tree diagram.

Holt Mathematics

12-4 Theoretical Probability

When you flip a fair coin, the *theoretical probability* of getting tails is 50% and the theoretical probability of getting heads is 50%. These two outcomes are equally likely to occur.

Determine whether the outcomes in each experiment are all equally likely to occur.

		Equally Likely	Not Equally Likely
1.		✓	
2.		✓	
3.			✓

Think and Discuss

4. Explain how you determined whether the outcomes in numbers **1–3** were equally likely or not.

Possible answer: If the figure or solid is divided into outcomes of equal sizes, each outcome will be equally likely. If the figure or solid is not divided equally, the outcomes will not all be equally likely to occur.

EXPLORATION

12-5 Compound Events

A *compound event* consists of two or more single events.

A bat had two babies. The birth of each baby bat is a single event. The birth of both bats is a compound event.

First bat born

	Female	Male
Female	FF	MF
Male	FM	MM

(Second bat born)

1. List all possible outcomes for two offspring. FF, MF, FM, MM

2. Divide 1 (FF) by the total number of outcomes to find the probability that both bats are female. $\frac{1}{4}$

3. Divide 1 (MM) by the total number of outcomes to find the probability that both bats are male. $\frac{1}{4}$

4. Divide 2 (MF and FM) by the total number of outcomes to find the probability that one bat is female and the other is male. $\frac{1}{2}$

Think and Discuss

5. **Explain** how to find the probability that three males would be born among four births. Possible answer: List all the possible outcomes. Count the number of outcomes that have three males. Then find the ratio of the number of such outcomes to the number of total outcomes.

Holt Mathematics

12-6 Making Predictions

You can use probabilities to make *predictions*. For example, the probability of rolling a 1 on a number cube is $\frac{1}{6}$. If you roll the cube 12 times, how many times do you predict you will roll a 1?

Each time you roll the cube, the probability of rolling a 1 is $\frac{1}{6}$.

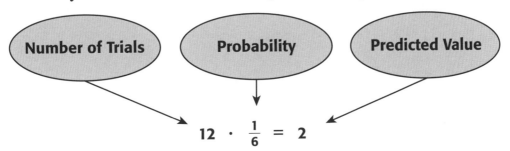

$$12 \cdot \frac{1}{6} = 2$$

So you expect to roll a 1 twice when you roll a cube 12 times.

Use the model as a guide to make each prediction.

	Event	Probability	Number of Trials	Predicted Value
1.	Getting heads when flipping a coin	$\frac{1}{2}$	Flip the coin 20 times.	10
2.	Spinning a 2 on a spinner divided into 4 equal sections	$\frac{1}{4}$	Spin the spinner 24 times.	6

Think and Discuss

3. **Explain** how to find a predicted value. Possible answer: Multiply the probability of the event by the number of trials.

4. **Discuss** whether it is certain that you will roll a 1 twice when you roll a number cube 12 times. Possible answer: It is not certain, but it is likely.

Holt Mathematics